SCHOLASTIC

ALL NEW 100 MATHS LESSONS

HOMEWORK & ASSESSMENT

YEAR 5

Scottish Primary 6

Yvette McDaniel

Credits

Author
Yvette McDaniel

Editor
Jo Kemp

Assistant Editor
Margaret Eaton

Illustrations
Andy Robb/Beehive Illustration
Jon Mitchell/Beehive Illustration

Series Designer
Catherine Mason

Designers
Melissa Leeke
Micky Pledge
Helen Taylor

Designed using Adobe InDesign

Published by Scholastic Ltd
Villiers House
Clarendon Avenue
Leamington Spa
Warwickshire CV32 5PR

www.scholastic.co.uk

Printed by Bell and Bain Ltd, Glasgow

1 2 3 4 5 6 7 8 9   6 7 8 9 0 1 2 3 4 5

British Library Cataloguing-in-Publication Data
A catalogue record for this book is available from the British Library.

ISBN 0-439-96517-9
ISBN 978-0439-96517-0

Contents

Contents

ASSESSMENT

About the series

All New100 Maths Homework and Assessment Activities offers a complete solution to your planning and resourcing for maths homework and assessment activities. There are seven books in the series, one for each year group from Reception to Year 6.

Each *All New 100 Maths Homework and Assessment Activities* book contains approximately 60 homework activities, with activity sheets to take home, and assessments for each half-term, end of term and end of year.

The homework and assessment activities support planning based on the National Numeracy Strategy's medium-term plans, but using the language of the learning objectives for that year as they appear in the NNS *Framework for Teaching Mathematics* (DfEE, 1999).

About the homework activities

Each homework activity is presented as a photocopiable page, with some supporting notes for parents and helpers provided underneath the activity. Teacher's notes appear in grid format for each term at the beginning of each term's activities. There are unit references in the grid, which link the homework activities to the relevant units in the NNS medium-term plan. Page references are also given that correspond to the relevant activities in the sister book, *All New 100 Maths Lessons Year 5* (Scholastic). The grid is the only place in the book where the objectives and further detail about the homework are provided. When exactly the homework is set and followed up is left to your professional judgement.

Across the *All New 100 Maths Homework and Assessment Activities* series, the homework activities cover the range of homework types suggested by the National Numeracy Strategy. For Year 5, there are Maths to share activities, Homework activities, Maths homework and Puzzles to do at home.

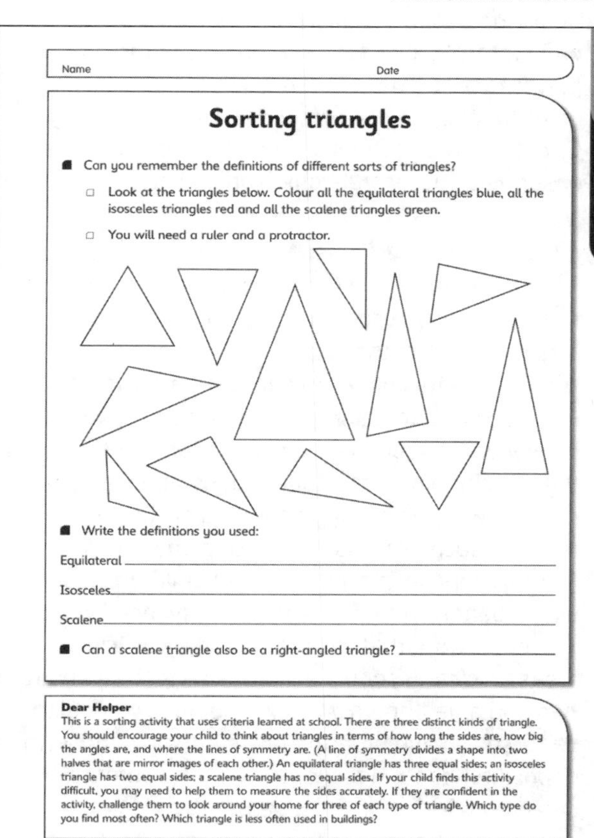

Name Date

AUTUMN HOMEWORK

Sorting triangles

- Can you remember the definitions of different sorts of triangles?
  - Look at the triangles below. Colour all the equilateral triangles blue, all the isosceles triangles red and all the scalene triangles green.
  - You will need a ruler and a protractor.

- Write the definitions you used:

Equilateral ______

Isosceles ______

Scalene ______

- Can a scalene triangle also be a right-angled triangle? ______

Dear Helper
This is a sorting activity that uses criteria learned at school. There are three distinct kinds of triangle. You should encourage your child to think about triangles in terms of how long the sides are, how big the angles are, and where the lines of symmetry are. (A line of symmetry divides a shape into two halves that are mirror images of each other.) An equilateral triangle has three equal sides; an isosceles triangle has two equal sides; a scalene triangle has no equal sides. If your child finds this activity difficult, you may need to help them to measure the sides accurately. If they are confident in the activity, challenge them to look around your home for three of each type of triangle. Which type do you find most often? Which triangle is less often used in buildings?

PHOTOCOPIABLE 25

www.scholastic.co.uk ALL NEW 100 MATHS HOMEWORK AND ASSESSMENT • YEAR 5

- **Maths to share activities** encourage the child to discuss the homework task with a parent or carer, and may, for example, involve the home context, or a game to be played with the carer.
- **Homework activities** are timed exercises which encourage the child to work rapidly.
- **Maths homework** activities allow the child to practise skills.
- **Puzzles to do at home** are investigations or problem-solving tasks. Again, the parent or carer is encouraged to be involved with the activity, offering support to the child, and discussing the activity and its outcomes with the child.

Using the homework activities

Each homework page includes a 'Helper note', which explains the aim of the homework and how the adult can support their child if he or she cannot get started. It is recommended that some form of homework diary be used alongside these activities, through which to establish an effective home-school dialogue about the children's enjoyment and understanding of the homework. A homework diary page is provided on page 8 of this book if you do not currently have another resource in use.

Teacher's notes

The teacher's notes appear at the start of each term's homework activities. They are presented in a grid format. The grid for the homework activities sets out the following:

- The title of the homework.
- Learning objectives: these are linked to the NNS medium-term plan. Where appropriate, the key objective(s) for that unit have a homework activity. This will help as part of on-going teacher assessment to show how well the children have understood the concepts being taught.
- The content of the homework: this shows the type of homework (Maths to share activities, Homework activities, Maths homework and Puzzles to do at home) and briefly describes the format and content of the activity.
- Managing the homework: this section provides 'before' and 'after' information for the teacher. The 'before' notes provide suggestions for ways to introduce and explain the homework before the children take it home. These notes might include a brief oral activity to undertake as preparation for the homework. The 'after' notes provide suggestions for how to manage the review of the homework when the children return with it to school. Suggestions include marking the work together, discussing strategies used for solving a problem, comparing solutions and playing a game as a class.
- NNS unit reference.
- Page link to *All New 100 Maths Lessons Year 5*. This will enable practitioners who are using this sister book to compare what is being taught that week with the homework, so that the teacher can decide which homework to choose and when to send it home.

Developing a homework policy

The homework activities have been written with the DfES 'Homework guidelines' in mind. These can be located in detail on the Standards Site: **www.standards.dfes.gov.uk/homework/goodpractice** The guidelines are a good starting point for planning an effective homework policy. Effective home-school partnerships are also vital in ensuring a successful homework policy.

Teacher's notes

Activity name	Learning objectives	Content of homework	Managing the homework	All New 100 Maths Lessons Year 5	
				NNS	Page
Investigating place value	• Read and write whole numbers in digits and words and know what each digit represents.	**Puzzles to do at home** Children reorder two, three or four given digits to make as many different numbers as possible.	**Before:** Ask the children to remind you of the strategies used in class to find the greatest and smallest numbers. **After:** Share results. Is the outcome the same with different digits?	1	8
Aim high	• Read and write whole numbers in digits and words and know what each digit represents.	**Maths to share** Place value game. Players use five 0–9 digits to make the highest number.	**Before:** Discuss the place value choices children face when they pick a high or low digit early in the game. **After:** Invite the children to tell you who won. Ask what difficult decisions they had to make (eg a middle-sized number early on).	1	8
Times-table challenge	• Know by heart multiplication facts up to 10 x 10.	**Maths homework** Timed completion of differentiated multiplication grids. The time should improve with practice.	**Before:** Stress the importance of instant recall, which means that children should not have to work out table facts. **After:** Record best times for future comparison. Invite the children to say some table fact questions for others to recall.	2	13
Doubling game	• Derive quickly or continue to derive quickly doubles of all whole numbers 1 to 100 and the corresponding halves.	**Maths to share** Children cut out given number cards; shuffle, pick one and begin to double, taking turns. First person to go over 100 gets a point. Repeat.	**Before:** Ask the children to remind you of some strategies for doubling more tricky numbers that bridge the next 10. **After:** Ask the children to list, as a class or group, the doubles that they can instantly recall.	2	15
Number creatures	• Derive quickly all two-digit pairs that total 100. • **Know by heart all multiplication facts up to 10 x 10.** • Continue to derive quickly division facts corresponding to tables up to 10 x 10.	**Maths homework** Provides opportunities to think creatively and use known number facts to develop number sentences.	**Before:** Make a link and recall known number facts, whether they are doubles, table facts or number bonds. **After:** Invite the children to share some of their number sentences for the rest of the class to complete.	3	23

HOMEWORK AUTUMN

9 ALL NEW 100 MATHS HOMEWORK AND ASSESSMENT • YEAR 5

Encouraging home-school links

An effective working partnership with parents and carers makes a positive impact upon children's attainment in mathematics. The homework activities in this book are part of that partnership. Parents and carers are given guidance on what the homework is about, and on how to be involved with the activity. There are suggestions for helping the children who are struggling with a particular concept, such as ways of counting on or back mentally, and extension ideas for children who would benefit from slightly more advanced work. The homework that is set across the curriculum areas for Year 5 should amount to a total of about two and a half hours a week. The homework diary page, sent home with the homework activity with opportunities for a response from the parents/carers, can be found on page 8.

The results from the assessment activities can also be used by the teacher in discussions with parents or carers. The outcomes of the activities, which cover the key objectives taught that half-term, term or year, will give good evidence for the teacher and parents/carers about how well the child is performing for the year group.

Using the activities with *All New 100 Maths Lessons Year 5*

The activities, both homework and assessment, fit the planning within *All New 100 Maths Lessons Year 5*. As teachers plan their work on a week-by-week basis, so the homework activities can be chosen to fit the appropriate unit of work. They may equally be used alongside the appropriate NNS units, as clearly indicated in the Teacher's notes at the beginning of each term.

For assessment, there are activities to support the 'Assessment lessons' built into the NNS medium-term plan, for example weeks 7 and 14 in the autumn term of Year 5. The assessment tasks are built around the key objectives taught during the preceding half-term and all objectives taught are covered in the appropriate assessment. Further information about using the assessment activities can be found on page 84.

Homework diary

Name of activity & date sent home	Child's comments		Helper's comments	Teacher's comments
	Write about what you enjoyed	Write about what you learned		

Activity name	Learning objectives	Content of homework	Managing the homework	All New 100 Maths Lessons Year 5	
				NNS	Page
Investigating place value	• Read and write whole numbers in digits and words and know what each digit represents.	**Puzzles to do at home** Children reorder two, three or four given digits to make as many different numbers as possible.	**Before:** Ask the children to remind you of the strategies used in class to find the greatest and smallest numbers. **After:** Share results. Is the outcome the same with different digits?	**1**	**8**
Aim high	• Read and write whole numbers in digits and words and know what each digit represents.	**Maths to share** Place value game. Players use five 0–9 digits to make the highest number.	**Before:** Discuss the place value choices children face when they pick a high or low digit early in the game. **After:** Invite the children to tell you who won. Ask what difficult decisions they had to make (eg a middle-sized number early on).	**1**	**8**
Times-table challenge	• Know by heart multiplication facts up to 10 x 10.	**Maths homework** Timed completion of differentiated multiplication grids. The time should improve with practice.	**Before:** Stress the importance of instant recall, which means that children should not have to work out table facts. **After:** Record best times for future comparison. Invite the children to say some table fact questions for others to recall.	**2**	**13**
Doubling game	• Derive quickly or continue to derive quickly doubles of all whole numbers 1 to 100 and the corresponding halves.	**Maths to share** Children cut out given number cards; shuffle, pick one and begin to double, taking turns. First person to go over 100 gets a point. Repeat.	**Before:** Ask the children to remind you of some strategies for doubling more tricky numbers that bridge the next 10. **After:** Ask the children to list, as a class or group, the doubles that they can instantly recall.	**2**	**15**
Number creatures	• Derive quickly all two-digit pairs that total 100. • **Know by heart all multiplication facts up to 10 x 10.** • Continue to derive quickly division facts corresponding to tables up to 10 x 10.	**Maths homework** Provides opportunities to think creatively and use known number facts to develop number sentences.	**Before:** Make a link and recall known number facts, whether they are doubles, table facts or number bonds. **After:** Invite the children to share some of their number sentences for the rest of the class to complete.	**3**	**23**

Teacher's notes

Activity name	Learning objectives	Content of homework	Managing the homework	All New 100 Maths Lessons Year 5	
				NNS	Page
Multiplication and division word problems	● **Use all four operations to solve simple word problems involving numbers and quantities based on 'real life', money and measures.**	**Maths homework** Provides opportunities to apply calculation methods in real-life situations and word problems.	**Before:** Ask the children to remind you of various strategies that they might use when solving word problems. **After:** Invite some of the children to demonstrate the method they chose to solve some of the word problems.	3	24
Shape fractions	● Recognise when two simple fractions are equivalent, including relating hundredths to tenths.	**Maths homework** Children match pictures and fractions.	**Before:** Suggest to the children that they match the shapes with a pencil line first, before colouring the shapes, to ensure each fraction has a matching shape. **After:** Ask for different choices of matching shapes. Ask which pictures had more than one fraction.	4	27
Find the triples	● Recognise when two simple fractions are equivalent, including relating hundredths to tenths. ● **Use decimal notation for tenths and hundredths.**	**Maths to share** Fractions, percentages and decimal Pelmanism game.	**Before:** Explain the rules of Pelmanism or 'Pairs'. **After:** Invite some children to say a fraction or decimal for the rest of the class to suggest its equivalent.	4	29
Quantities for a recipe	● Solve simple problems using ideas of ratio and proportion (one for every..., one in every...).	**Maths to share** A simple recipe is given that makes six cakes. Children increase the quantities to make 12 or 18 cakes.	**Before:** Emphasise the safety aspect of baking at home. Stress that an adult must be consulted. **After:** Invite the children to suggest a ratio for decorating their cakes, eg cherries to buttons 1:4, and the rest of the class to calculate the numbers needed for 6, 12 and 18 cakes.	5	36
Ratio patterns	● Solve simple problems using ideas of ratio and proportion (one for every..., one in every...).	**Puzzles to do at home** Children colour given geometric patterns in a ratio of 3:2; 3:6.	**Before:** Ask the children to explain what a ratio is and how this will help them to colour their designs. **After:** Ask the children to calculate the total number of each colour used and express each colour as a proportion.	5	36
Comparing data	● Solve a problem by representing and interpreting data on a bar line chart where the vertical axis is labelled in 2s, 5s, 10s, 20s or 100s, where intermediate points may have meaning.	**Maths homework** Two line graphs displayed together on one page, with questions to answer.	**Before:** Ask the children to study the questions and to tell you the meaning of vocabulary such as 'difference', line graph and bar line graph. **After:** Invite some children to share further questions that could have been asked about this graph, for others to answer.	6	42

Teacher's notes

Activity name	Learning objectives	Content of homework	Managing the homework	All New 100 Maths Lessons Year 5	
				NNS	**Page**
Collecting and representing data	• Solve a problem by representing and interpreting data on a bar line chart where the vertical axis is labelled in 2s, 5s, 10s, 20s or 100s, where intermediate points may have meaning.	**Puzzles to do at home** Children set themselves a question and then collect data to answer it. They collect the information on a tally chart and decide on the most suitable type of graph to represent their information, then draw the graph.	**Before:** Make a class list of all the different suggestions the children can make about data that could be collected and represented as a graph. **After:** Make a class display. Ask some children to present their findings to the rest of the class.	6	42
Sorting triangles	• Classify triangles using criteria such as equal sides, equal angles, lines of symmetry. • Explain reasoning orally or in writing.	**Maths homework** Sorting triangles. Can a scalene triangle also be a right-angled triangle?	**Before:** Ask the children to tell you some properties for each of the triangles. **After:** Ask the children how many of each they found. Were there any that they were unsure about?	8	48
Perimeter problem	• **Use all four operations to solve simple word problems involving numbers and quantities.** • Choose and use appropriate number operations to solve problems, and appropriate ways of calculating.	**Maths homework** Word problems to calculate perimeter.	**Before:** Ask the children to remind you about ways of finding side lengths from a given perimeter. **After:** Compare results. Ask: *Which field would Ermintrude prefer? Why?*	9	59
Weights and measures	• Use, read and write standard metric units, including abbreviations and relationships between them. Convert larger units to smaller units. • Know imperial units.	**Puzzles to do at home** Children look in cupboards at home or go shopping to find out what measures items are generally sold in. Are there any standard quantities?	**Before:** Emphasise the permission issue and the safety warning regarding cleaning materials. **After:** Invite the children to make generalisations. Display their findings.	9	55
24 hours	• Use units of time on 24-hour digital clock and use 24-hour clock notation. Use timetables.	**Maths to share** Children create a 24-hour map of what you might be doing at given times.	**Before:** Ask the children to remind you of times of the day in the 24-hour clock system. **After:** Display the results.	10	62

Teacher's notes

Activity name	Learning objectives	Content of homework	Managing the homework	All New 100 Maths Lessons Year 5	
				NNS	Page
Telling the time	• Use units of time; read the time on a 24-hour digital clock and use 24-hour clock notation. Use timetables.	**Puzzles to do at home** Children collect examples of places around the home or town that use 24-hour digital notation and those that use the 12-hour am and pm system. Suggest reasons.	**Before:** Discuss places that need to display times. **After:** Share the class findings. Discuss why the system used might have been chosen.	10	62
The differences game	• Find differences by counting up through next multiple of 10, 100 or 1000.	**Maths to share** A game to encourage children to count on aloud, either in their heads or supported by a number line.	**Before:** Remind the children about counting on in 'jumps' to round up to the next 10, 100 etc. **After:** Ask the children to explain how they calculated. Can they suggest a rule to help someone else?	11	70
Take it away!	• **Extend written methods to column addition/ subtraction of two integers less than 10,000.**	**Maths homework** Opportunities to use the vertical subtraction methods used in class, whether the expanded or the compact methods.	**Before:** Remind the children to use the method that they have been working on in class and not to be tempted to try somebody else's 'easier' method. **After:** Ask individuals to demonstrate the methods they prefer. Troubleshoot any difficulties.	11	71
Magic squares	• Solve mathematical problems or puzzles, recognise and explain patterns and relationships, generalise and predict.	**Puzzles to do at home** Children investigate number patterns and attempt to explain and predict.	**Before:** Explain the rules of magic squares. **After:** Share some examples. Discuss whether there is more than one solution to the squares.	12	79
Number chains	• Recognise and extend number sequences formed by counting from any number in steps of constant size, extending beyond zero when counting back.	**Maths homework** Children spot the pattern and complete the sequence. Opportunities to create own patterns.	**Before:** Do some examples of these types of number patterns together. Discuss some strategies and things to look for. **After:** Hear some examples and invite the children to challenge each other with their own examples. Ask them to explain the 'key' or 'rule' to their patterns.	12	76

Name Date

Investigating place value

- From the digits given, list all the numbers that you can possibly make.
  - List them in ascending order, smallest first.
  - How many numbers can you make with each set of digits?

Two digits

2 8 ____________________ 6 7 ____________________

Three digits

4 5 9 ____________________

6 1 8 ____________________

Four digits

5 8 7 3 ____________________

____

____

____

7 0 4 3 ____________________

____

____

____

Dear Helper

This activity will encourage your child to think about the place value of each digit (what its value is in the number). A 5 in the units column is less in value than a 5 in the tens column, which is worth 50. If your child finds the numbers difficult to write in order, encourage them to partition each number (for example, 364 = 300 + 60 + 4) and look for the number with the smallest digit in the first column: this is the smallest number. Doing this will help your child to see the number order. If your child finds the activity easy, challenge them to find out whether the number of possible digits would be the same with different digits.

Name Date

Aim high

A game for two players.

- Cut out two sets of 0–9 digit cards.
  - Shuffle them, then place them face down on the table.
  - Ask your helper to play this game with you.
  - The aim is to see who can make the biggest number.
  - Take turns to choose a card and decide where to place it on your grid.

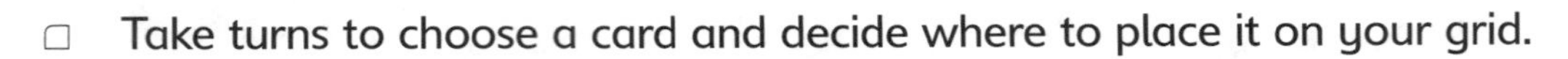

- Play the best of five games.

Player 1

Player 2

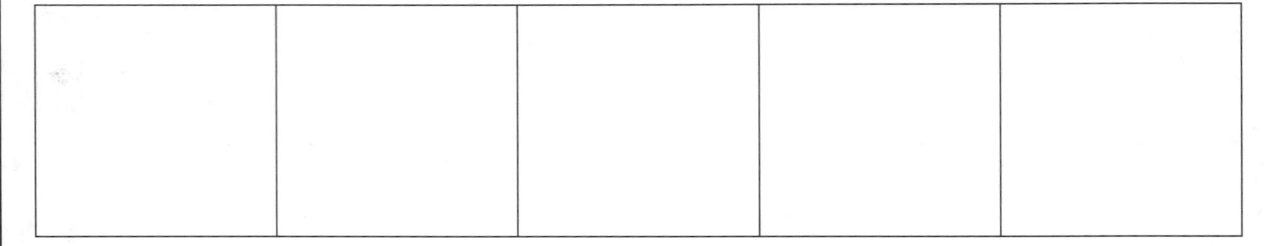

Dear Helper

Encourage your child to consider the place value of each box in the grid. From the left, the boxes are worth: tens of thousands, thousands, hundreds, tens, units. You could write TTh, Th, H, T, U above the appropriate boxes to support your child if they are finding this activity difficult. In order to get the biggest possible number, you should give any high digit you pick a high place value and give any low digit a lower place value. If your child finds this activity easy, challenge them to work out the difference between the two numbers each time.

Name Date

Times-table challenge

- How fast can you complete each times-table grid?
  - Write your time at the bottom.
  - Now colour in all the square numbers.

×	2	3	4	5	6	7	8
2							
4							
8							
3							
6							
9							

Time: ____________________

×	3	4	5	6	7	8	9
4							
5							
9							
3							
7							
2							

Time: ____________________

×	4	5	6	7	8	9	10
2							
3							
4							
5							
6							
7							

Time: ____________________

×	6	5	7	8	9	3	4
8							
4							
5							
9							
7							
6							

Time: ____________________

Dear Helper

This homework should be timed. Your child's speed should improve with practice. It is not necessary for your child to complete all four grids at one sitting. It would be helpful to do some learning practice with your child after they complete each grid. This could take the form of you calling out quick-fire times-tables questions, such as: *What is 3 × 4?* or *How many 5s in 25?* It is not enough to be able to find the answer by chanting through the tables, because an instant response is required (though knowing the tables is a good starting point). If your child is confident with 10 times-table facts, challenge them to try multiplying 11, 12 or 13 by 2, 3, 4, 5 and 6. Use an extra sheet for this purpose.

Name Date

Doubling game

- It is possible to play this game on your own, but it is more fun with someone else!
  - Cut out the cards below and shuffle them.
  - Turn them face down, then take a card and double it.
  - Your helper then doubles your total, then you double theirs, and so on.
  - The first player to get past 100 wins a point.
  - Pick another card and start again.
  - Write down what numbers you make.
- The winner is the player with more points when you have used all the cards.

1	2	3	4
5	6	7	8
9	10	11	12
13	14	15	16

Dear Helper

The point of this game is for your child to practise recalling doubles that they already know, and to increase their speed and efficiency with more difficult ones where the number has to be partitioned (split). For example, double 37 = double 30 + double 7 = 60 + 14 = 74. Look for realistic answers. You could also remind your child to check that their answers are realistic by estimating – for example, double 37 will be more than double 35 and less than double 40. If your child can complete this task easily, alter the number cards to make them into two- or three-digit numbers and aim for a total of 500.

Name Date

Number creatures

- Complete the number creature for each of these numbers by writing as many different number sentences as you can to make that number.
- An example has been done for you.

Dear Helper
This activity helps your child to think about all four number operations (+, –, ×, ÷) and be inventive about using them. Try to discourage your child from simply adding 1 or taking away 1. If your child is finding the activity difficult, use counters or coins to help them get a visual image of the numbers. If your child is confident with making number sentences, challenge them to attempt two-step operations – for example, making 35 by doubling 15 and then adding 5.

Name Date

Multiplication and division word problems

Potatoes 90p per kg
Oranges 12p each
Tomatoes 86p per kg
Pineapples £2.50 each
Apples £1.60 per kg
Broccoli 98p per kg
Onions 48p per kg
Carrots 36p per kg
Bananas £2.40 per kg

- Answer these questions.
- Show how you worked them out.
- You can use different methods to answer different questions.

1. How much do these things cost?

5kg of potatoes	Six oranges	Four pineapples	500g of bananas

2. How much do these things cost?

One banana if five bananas weigh 1kg	One apple if four apples weigh 1kg	4kg of carrots	3kg of tomatoes

3. I am going to make some soup for my friends. This is the recipe. How much will it cost me to buy all the vegetables?

500g carrots
2kg potatoes
500g onions
3kg tomatoes

Dear Helper

This activity will help your child to use different methods for multiplication and division. Please encourage your child to use the methods learned at school, such as the grid method for multiplying, or division by 'chunking' (ie dividing part of the number using a known times-table, and then subtracting it from the original number). If your child is unable to remember a method, please do not try to teach them the way you were taught as this will only lead to confusion. If your child finds these calculations difficult, encourage them to multiply by repeated addition, or by counting in steps (of 2, 3 and so on). A more able child could be encouraged to make up further, more complicated shopping list calculations.

Name Date

Shape fractions

- Shade part of each shape and match the shape fraction to the appropriate number fraction.
- Draw a line to join each pair together.

Warning: some shape fractions may match more than one number fraction!

Shapes	Fractions
	$\frac{2}{5}$ $\frac{3}{2}$ $1\frac{2}{3}$
	$\frac{7}{5}$ $\frac{5}{8}$ $\frac{3}{3}$
	$1\frac{15}{10}$
	$1\frac{3}{4}$ $\frac{10}{6}$ $1\frac{1}{2}$
	$\frac{3}{4}$ $1\frac{5}{8}$ $\frac{1}{2}$
	$1\frac{13}{8}$

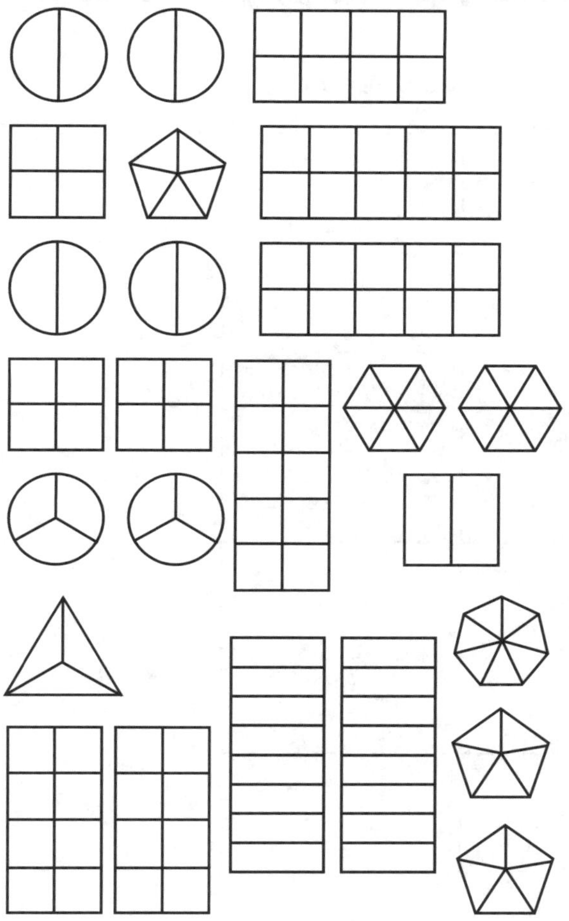

Dear Helper

This activity helps your child to recall how fractions can appear visually, as parts of shapes, and to recognise equivalent fractions in the form of improper fractions (eg $^{13}/_{5}$) and mixed numbers (eg $2^{3}/_{5}$). If your child is unable to remember how to convert from one to the other, remind them that the bottom number in a fraction is the number of pieces the shape has been cut into and the top number is the number of pieces they have got. So the improper fraction $^{3}/_{2}$, for example, is larger than 1. Fractions such as $^{3}/_{3}$, $^{4}/_{4}$ and $^{5}/_{5}$ are all equal to 1. As a challenge, suggest that your child tries to draw and name some shapes of their own.

Name Date

Find the triples

This is a game for two to four players.

- Cut out the cards carefully and shuffle the pack.
  - Place all the cards face down, spread evenly across the table.
  - Take turns to turn over three cards.
  - If all three cards are equivalent in value (for example, $\frac{1}{2}$ = 0.5 = 50%), keep them. If not, turn them back.
  - The aim is to collect as many families of three as you can.

$\frac{1}{10}$	0.1	10%	$\frac{2}{10}$	0.2
20%	$\frac{1}{4}$	0.25	25%	$\frac{1}{2}$
0.5	50%	$\frac{3}{10}$	0.3	
30%	$\frac{3}{4}$	0.75	75%	

Dear Helper

Please play this game with your child. Before you play, it might be helpful to make sure that you are both familiar with the equivalent values (for example, $^2/_{10}$ = 20% = 0.2 and ¼ = 0.25 = 25%). This activity will help your child to recognise equivalent fractions, decimals and percentages and be able to swap from one to another when calculating. If your child has difficulty recognising all three equivalents, remove the percentage cards to begin with and remind them to convert all the fractions to tenths to work out the decimal. A further challenge might be to extend the pack by finding other decimal equivalents, using a calculator and converting them to percentages.

Name Date

Quantities for a recipe

- Here is a recipe to make six small sponge cakes.
- How would you increase the quantities of the ingredients to make 12 or 18 cakes?
  - Remember to keep the quantities of the different ingredients in the same ratio.

To make 6 small sponge cakes, you will need:	To make 12 small sponge cakes, you will need:	To make 18 small sponge cakes, you will need:
50g self-raising flour	______ g self-raising flour	______ g self-raising flour
50g soft margarine	______ g soft margarine	______ g soft margarine
50g caster sugar	______ g caster sugar	______ g caster sugar
1 egg	______ eggs	______ eggs
1 tablespoon cocoa	______ tablespoons cocoa	______ tablespoons cocoa
6 paper cake cases	______ paper cake cases	______ paper cake cases

SAFETY WARNING: Ask an adult to help you with the hot oven.

Wash your hands before you start. However many cakes you make, the method is the same.

1. Beat the margarine and sugar together in a large mixing bowl until the mixture is smooth and creamy. You can do this with a wooden spoon or an electric whisk.
2. Beat in the egg, a little at a time. If the mixture becomes wet and slimy, beat in a spoonful of the flour.
3. When all the egg has been mixed in, sieve the flour and cocoa into the mixture and stir in gently with a large metal spoon.
4. Place the cake cases in a cake tin and divide the mixture between the cases.
5. Bake in a hot oven at 180°C (or gas mark 5) for 12 to 15 minutes.
6. Your cakes are cooked when they are bouncy and springy to the touch. Leave them to cool on a wire rack. The cakes can be eaten as they are, or with a little icing on the top.

Dear Helper
This activity demonstrates one way that ratios are used in daily life. The recipe will not work if the amount of one ingredient is increased without increasing the other ingredients in the same proportion. If you and your child make the cakes, show them how to work safely and hygienically in the kitchen, then share the cakes! Children who find this easy might enjoy converting other recipes, eg altering quantities for a curry for four people to make it for six or two or three people.

Name Date

Ratio patterns

- Colour these two patterns.
- For each pattern, use two colours in the given ratio.

A ratio of 3:2

A ratio of 3:6

Dear Helper
If your child is unsure how to colour in the patterns, please remind them that a ratio is 'one for every...'. So, for example, a ratio of 2:3 would be 2 red pieces for every 3 green pieces. To challenge your child further, encourage them to look for ratio patterns in everyday life – for example, pieces of cutlery to plates at the table, or sausages to eggs on a plate.

Name Date

Comparing data

- Look at these two line graphs. They show the temperatures in London and Athens over one 12-hour period in summer.
  - ▢ Use the graphs to answer the questions below.
  - ▢ Write on the back of this sheet.

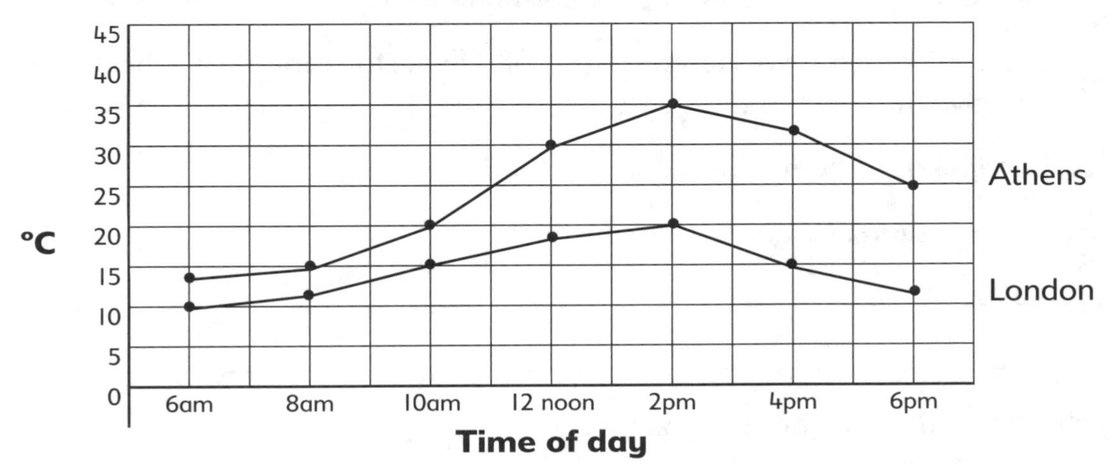

Questions

1. What is the difference between the highest temperatures shown in Athens and London?
2. What is the difference between the highest and lowest temperatures in London?
3. What is the temperature in both cities at 5:00pm?
4. Why is this information displayed as a line graph, not a bar chart or a bar line graph?
5. Give two examples of situations where a bar line graph would be appropriate, and two where a line graph should be used.

Dear Helper

A line graph is used to show how something measurable, such as a person's temperature, changes over a period of time. A bar chart or a bar line graph is used to compare numbers of separate things, such as cars or different-colour eyes. To help your child understand this, it may be helpful to explain that temperature never goes away: it may rise and fall, but it is always there and can be measured at all times. You may be able to help a child who finds reading the scale difficult by dividing the space between values with four small lines or divisions to enable them to work out the temperature by counting on in ones. Challenge your child to write some more questions for you to answer, using the graphs.

Name Date

Collecting and representing data

- Collect data about something that interests you.
- Set yourself a question to answer, for example, 'What is the most popular type of vehicle that passes my house in an hour?' or 'How many of the different types of minibeasts can I find in one area of the garden?'
  - ☐ Collect the information in a tally chart (see below), then decide on the best type of graph to represent your information.
  - ☐ Draw the graph on a separate sheet of paper. Don't forget to label the axes and give the graph a title.
  - ☐ Can you use it to answer your question?

The question I want to investigate:

____

____

Tally chart: Use as much of this as you need.

My results: I found out that...

____

____

Dear Helper
This activity will help your child to collect data and draw a graph in order to answer a question. Any question along the lines of 'How many...', 'How high...', 'Which is the most popular?' will be appropriate. The investigation is in two parts: collecting data and recording it in a tally chart, then drawing a graph. Please remind your child that a line graph is the best way to show measurable data that changes with time, such as temperature; a bar line graph is best for comparing different items, such as types of minibeasts or cars. If your child finds the concepts of graphs difficult, choose only a small number of comparisons and number the vertical axis in ones. A more challenging graph might be one where there is a very high number of items to be counted, where the vertical axis would need to be labelled as one square for every 5 or 10, thus requiring estimation.

Name Date

Sorting triangles

- Can you remember the definitions of different sorts of triangles?
  - Look at the triangles below. Colour all the equilateral triangles blue, all the isosceles triangles red and all the scalene triangles green.
  - You will need a ruler and a protractor.

- Write the definitions you used:

Equilateral ____________________

Isosceles ____________________

Scalene ____________________

- Can a scalene triangle also be a right-angled triangle? ____________________

Dear Helper

This is a sorting activity that uses criteria learned at school. There are three distinct kinds of triangle. You should encourage your child to think about triangles in terms of how long the sides are, how big the angles are, and where the lines of symmetry are. (A line of symmetry divides a shape into two halves that are mirror images of each other.) An equilateral triangle has three equal sides; an isosceles triangle has two equal sides; a scalene triangle has no equal sides. If your child finds this activity difficult, you may need to help them to measure the sides accurately. If they are confident in the activity, challenge them to look around your home for three of each type of triangle. Which type do you find most often? Which triangle is less often used in buildings?

Name Date

Perimeter problem

- Alfred the farmer has a tricky problem. He has 30m of fencing wire to make an enclosure for his pet goat Ermintrude.
  - ☐ Draw as many different rectangles as you can, using units of 1 metre.
  - ☐ Label them with the side lengths.
  - ☐ Use 1cm to represent 1m in your drawings.
  - ☐ Remember that all the rectangles must have a 30m perimeter.
  - ☐ Use more sheets of paper if necessary.

14m

1m

- How many diffferent rectangles could Alfred make? ____________________

Dear Helper

Please help your child to be systematic in working out this problem. A rectangle always has two pairs of opposite sides of equal length, and all the corners are right angles. If your child is finding this difficult, encourage them to start with two sides measuring 1cm – that uses up 2cm of the possible 30cm, leaving 28cm for the other two sides (14cm each). Then move on systematically, increasing the first two sides to 2cm, and so on. As a challenge ask: *How many more dimensions can you discover if you use decimal fractions of a metre?*

Name Date

Weights and measures

- With an adult, look in your store cupboards at home, or accompany an adult when they go shopping.
  - Find out what weights and measures packaged items are generally sold in.
  - You might like to use the shopping list below, or make up a list of your own. (WARNING: Avoid cleaning materials or other products that might be dangerous.)
  - In the space at the bottom of this sheet, write about what you have found.
  - Are there any standard quantities for items? For example, is milk always sold in the same quantity (or multiples of that quantity)?

My research shopping list	Weights and measures
jam	
washing powder	
milk	
fizzy drink	
flour	
sugar	
rice	
soup	
tinned tomatoes	
baked beans	

What I found out:

Dear Helper
Most items we buy are available in certain standard amounts, and in this activity, your child is finding out about how weights and measures are standardised. You can help by letting your child look in your food cupboards and pointing out similarities to them – for example, tins are generally in one of three standard sizes. Encourage your child to look for general trends in the weights and measures they see. Challenge them to find out how many servings each container holds. They can also work out how many of each item they would need to buy to feed 50 people.

Name Date

24 hours

- Use the circle below to keep a diary of your activities for a day at the weekend.
- You could divide the hours into 30 minutes to be more accurate.

00:00
midnight

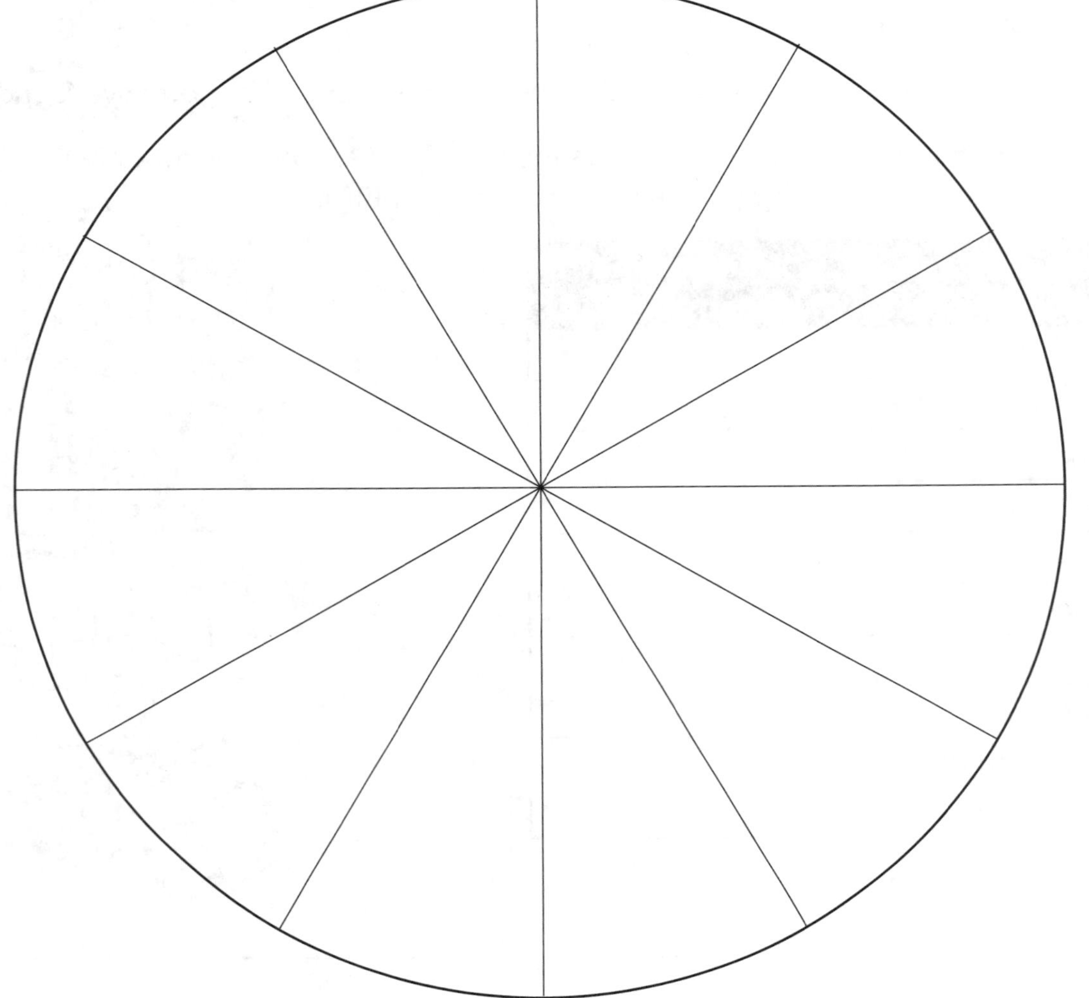

Dear Helper
This activity will help your child to learn the 24-hour digital system. Please encourage your child to use the 24-hour clock when thinking about times. Perhaps you could remind them of this when saying the time in the afternoon or evening: instead of saying *It is 7:00 in the evening*, you could say *It is 19:00*. If your child finds the 24-hour clock difficult, remind them that a 24-hour day is two sets of 12 hours, the first up to 12 noon and the second from noon until midnight. You might help them by drawing them these two 12-hour clocks side by side. Challenge your child by asking them to be more precise, giving their activity times in hours and minutes.

Name Date

Telling the time

- Look around your home and town to find examples of some places that use the 24-hour system for telling the time and other places that use the 12-hour system.

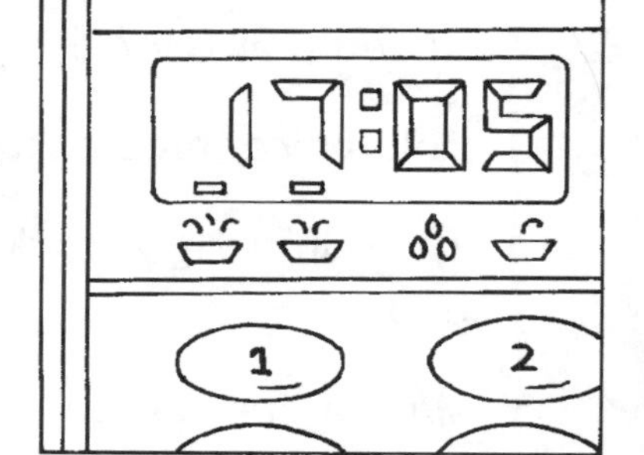

  - ☐ You might look at newspapers, timetables, clocks and shops.
  - ☐ Record these places in the table below.
  - ☐ Can you suggest a reason why that particular system of time-telling was chosen?

Place	12-hour or 24-hour system?	Why?

Dear Helper
This observation activity helps your child to see the two different time systems in real-life contexts. Encourage your child to think about the reasons for using each system. For example, train timetables tend to use the 24-hour clock system to avoid confusion between morning and evening. Shops are generally only open in the daytime, and so only need to use the 12-hour system. Challenge your child to use the 24-hour system when telling the time and arranging activities this week.

Name Date

The differences game

- You need a dice for this game.
  - Roll a dice three or four times to generate a three-digit or four-digit number.
  - The number you make must be smaller than the number in the middle of the grid.
  - Write your number on the left-hand side in the spaces provided.
  - Calculate the difference between the two numbers, and write it in the space on the right.
- The first one has been done for you.

Dice number								Difference
1	7	6	8	2	0	0	4	236
				4	0	1	3	
				5	0	0	7	
				4	0	0	1	
				5	0	0	2	
				1	0	0	9	
				3	0	1	5	
				4	0	0	8	
				5	0	0	6	

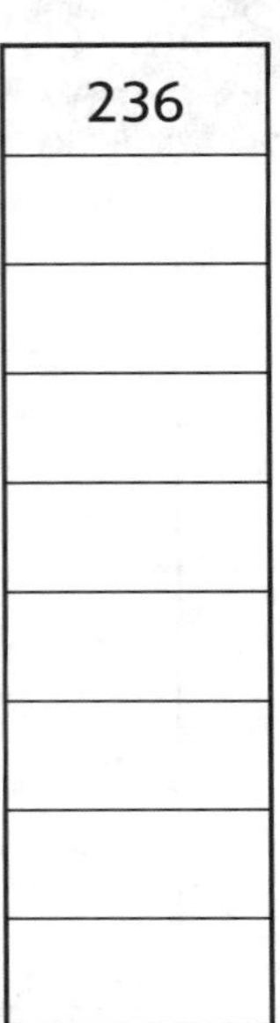

- Here is a number line to show the first subtraction. Draw your own number lines if they will help you to work out the other subtractions.

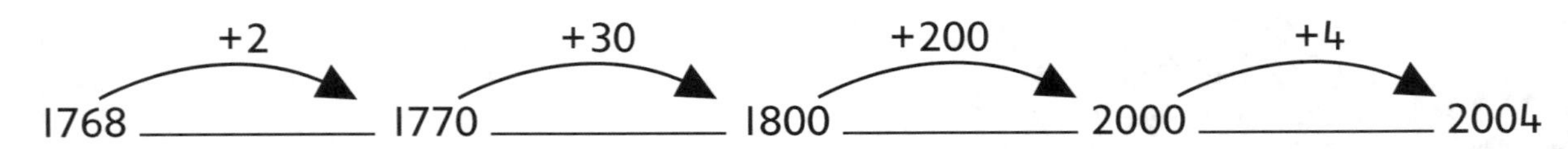

Dear Helper
This activity will help your child to practise counting on from a smaller number to a larger one, 'bridging' through the next 10, 100 or 1000 in between. It is not a written subtraction test. If your child cannot find the difference mentally, encourage them to use 'jumps' on a number line as in the example provided. You could challenge your child to calculate these 'jumps' mentally, using informal notes of the numbers rather than a number line.

Name Date

Take it away!

- Use the written vertical method of subtraction that you have learned at school to do these calculations.

1.

H	T	U
5	7	4
− 3	3	2

2.

H	T	U
8	2	7
− 4	1	4

3.

Th	H	T	U
2	4	6	1
− 1	3	4	7

4.

Th	H	T	U
3	5	1	4
− 1	3	6	7

5.

H	T	U
8	9	2
− 4	2	3

6.

Th	H	T	U
3	5	7	9
− 2	7	5	1

7. An outward flight to America carries 427 people. The return flight carries 579 people.

a) What is the total number of people carried on the two flights? ____________________

b) What is the difference between the number of people on the outward flight and the number on the return flight? ____________________

Dear Helper

Your child has been learning in school a variety of methods for doing written subtraction with large numbers. Encourage them to partition and redistribute the numbers, as they have been shown. Children who are having difficulty may need reminding that partitioning means: 3432 = 3000 + 400 + 30 + 2. These numbers can be redistributed, eg 3432 = 2000 + 1300 + 130 + 2 or 2000 + 1400 + 20 + 12. Also remind them to avoid taking the top number away from the bottom one by mistake. Unfortunately, the method of written subtraction that you learned at school may confuse your child. Let them teach you their method! Challenge your child to make up a five- or six-digit subtraction that needs all the digits redistributing and then solve it!

Name Date

Magic squares

- This is a 'magic square' (see right).
  - The total of the numbers in every row, column and diagonal is the same number: 15.
  - 15 is the 'magic total' for this square.

4	3	8
9	5	1
2	7	6

- Write down four things that you observe about this magic square. For example, you might observe that the four corner numbers are even.

1. ______
2. ______
3. ______
4. ______

- Can you make up two more magic squares in the grids below, using the numbers 1 to 9?
  - The 'magic total' can be 15 or any other number.
  - Cut out the digit cards below to help you re-arrange the numbers.

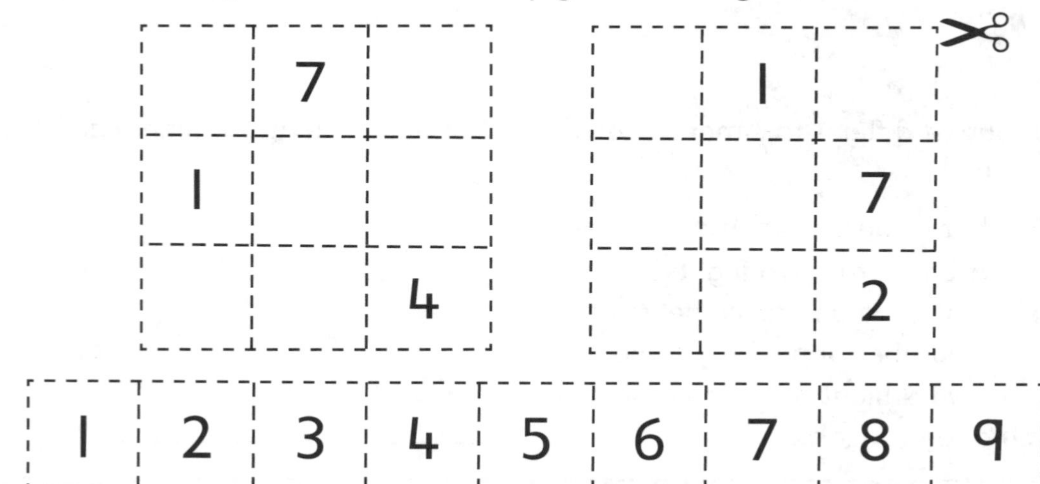

	7	
1		
		4

	1	
		7
		2

1	2	3	4	5	6	7	8	9

Dear Helper
Your child will have to solve this puzzle by using trial and error and remembering the rule of a magic square: that the numbers in all rows, columns and diagonals add up to the same total. Your child should be able to use knowledge of how numbers combine to help with this – for example, knowing that two odd numbers add to make an even number. If your child finds this difficult, show them that odd numbers often go in the corners and even ones in the middle. Challenge your child to make up a magic square with a different total number.

Name Date

Number chains

- Can you spot the pattern in each chain?
  - Add more links to each chain, filling in the spaces.

1.

1	1	1	2	1	1	1	2			

2.

3	3	2	1	3	3				

3.

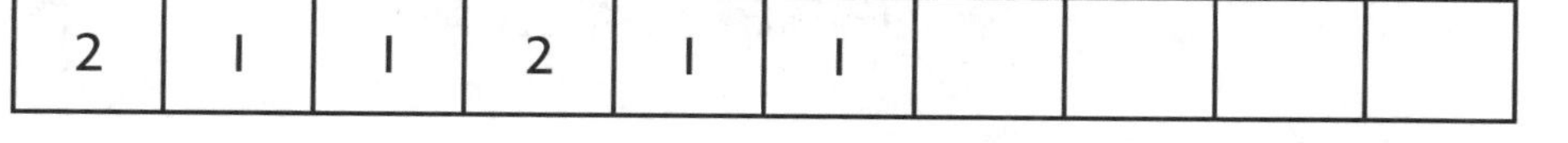

2	1	1	2	1	1				

4. 18, 23, 28, 33, 38, ______, ______, ______

5. 132, 122, 112, 102, 92, ______, ______, ______

6. 6, 3, 0, –3, –6, ______, ______, ______

7. 1, 2, 4, 7, 11, 16, 22, ______, ______, ______

- Now make up some number chains of your own.

Dear Helper

Number chains can be made by adding a number each time, but they can also be made with a more complex sequence, such as a sequence of square numbers. Help your child to think about the differences between successive numbers in the chain: they do not necessarily have to be of a constant size. If your child finds these chains difficult to see, write in the differences between the successive numbers to help them recognise a pattern. A more challenging pattern might be to double the previous number and add a constant number to it. Encourage your child to be inventive.

Teacher's notes

Activity name	Learning objectives	Content of homework	Managing the homework	All New 100 Maths Lessons Year 5	
				NNS	**Page**
Where is the hottest place?	• **Order a given set of positive and negative integers.**	**Puzzles to do at home** Children use < and > to write statements about temperatures and order them.	**Before:** Ask the children to remind you of the meanings of the < and > symbols. **After:** Link to geography: ask where you should go to ski or to get a sun tan etc. Use an atlas.	**1**	**86**
Tables builder	• Use closely related facts.	**Puzzles to do at home** Build knowledge of 12, 13 and 14 times-tables from known facts of 10 and 2, 3 or 4 times-tables.	**Before:** Ask the children to remind you of useful links between times-tables that they have recently explored. **After:** Invite the children to suggest further developments using these links, such as to multiples of 22, 24 or 26.	**2**	**91**
Use what you know	• Use factors (eg $8 \times 12 = 8 \times 4 \times 3$). • Begin to use brackets. • Use closely related facts.	**Maths homework** Multiplying using factors. Multiplying by near multiples of 10 and adjusting.	**Before:** Ask the children to explain to you what a factor is and how it can help us to multiply. **After:** Discuss the strategies used and discover preferences.	**2**	**89**
Sort them out	• Choose and use appropriate number operations to solve problems, and appropriate ways of calculating: mental, mental with jottings, written methods, calculator.	**Puzzles to do at home** Children use the headings of the given square to work out the only numbers (1 to 16) that could fit into the square.	**Before:** Ask the children to explain the meaning of the vocabulary used in the puzzle. **After:** Share results. Invite individuals to explain their thinking when they decided on placing the numbers.	**3**	**98**
Charlie's chocolate chips	• Choose and use appropriate number operations to solve problems, and appropriate ways of calculating: mental, mental with jottings, written methods, calculator.	**Puzzles to do at home** An investigation to test knowledge of multiples, division and problem-solving strategies.	**Before:** Explain to the children that they need to show how they solve this problem. **After:** Invite the children to explain their strategies.	**3**	**99**

Activity name	Learning objectives	Content of homework	Managing the homework	All New 100 Maths Lessons Year 5	
				NNS	**Page**
Fractions and decimals	• **Relate fractions to division,** and use division to find simple fractions.	**Maths homework** Children link fractions to their equivalent decimals ($^{1}/_{10}$ and $^{1}/_{100}$) and known partners (eg ½ = $^{5}/_{10}$ = 0.5).	**Before:** Ask the children to remind you how a calculator can assist when finding fraction/decimal equivalents. **After:** Ask the children how many fraction/decimal equivalents they can remember.	4	103
Ordering masses	• Order a set of numbers or measurements with the same number of decimal places.	**Maths to share** Children order weights of food packages at home by converting all into decimal kg from g – for example, 500g = 0.5kg.	**Before:** Stress the health and safety implications of this activity and the importance of adult permission. **After:** It can be interesting to amalgamate some of the homework results into a class weights and measures number line.	4	106
Looking at lines	• Recognise positions and directions; **recognise perpendicular and parallel lines.**	**Puzzles to do at home** Children list parallel and perpendicular lines in their house.	**Before:** Ask the children to remind you of the definitions of parallel and perpendicular. **After:** Invite the children to share their observations. Were there many examples where lines were both parallel and perpendicular?	5	112
Finding areas	• **Understand and use the formula in words 'length x breadth' for the area of a rectangle.**	**Maths homework** Children find the area of given shapes and convert to the equivalent unit of measure if necessary.	**Before:** Ask the children to remind you of the difficulties involved in mixed-unit calculations. **After:** Invite some of the children to describe how they found the area of shapes that were not rectangles.	7	120
Living space	• **Understand and use the formula in words 'length x breadth' for the area of a rectangle.**	**Maths to share** Children draw an approximate plan of a room in their house and find the area by dividing it into rectangles.	**Before:** Advise the children that they may have to round some of their measurements. Revise how to do this. **After:** Invite the children to discuss any difficulties they had.	7	121

Teacher's notes

Activity name	Learning objectives	Content of homework	Managing the homework	All New 100 Maths Lessons Year 5	
				NNS	Page
Access all areas	• **Understand area measured in square centimetres (cm^2).**	**Puzzles to do at home** Children research how many things are sold in cm^2, m^2 or km^2 and collect evidence (eg advertisements).	**Before:** Have a class sharing session where the children suggest places to look for this information. **After:** Use some of their findings in a display or a class area/book.	7	119
Missing data	• Solve a problem by representing and interpreting data in tables, charts, graphs and diagrams.	**Maths homework** Children add missing information to a variety of graphs.	**Before:** Look at the graphs and point out the information that is given in the graphs. **After:** Have a class sharing session. A wide variety of suggestions will demonstrate why labels and titles are so important.	8	125
Fruit facts	• Solve a problem by representing and interpreting data in tables, charts, graphs and diagrams.	**Maths homework** Children use given graphs to interpret and find information.	**Before:** Ask the children to tell you how to draw a comparative bar chart and remind you how to find the median. **After:** Discuss any difficulties.	8	126
Double dice	• Identify near doubles. • Use informal paper and pencil methods to support, record or explain additions and subtractions.	**Maths to share** Children play the dice doubling game at home to encourage use of doubling as a strategy for adding.	**Before:** Demonstrate how to generate the numbers, arrange and round for Game 2. **After:** Ask: *What was the highest score reached in Game 1? What was the highest possible score in Game 2?*	9	132
Calculations page	• **Extend written methods to column addition/ subtraction of two integers less than 10,000.**	**Maths homework** Consolidation of written addition and subtraction methods learned in class.	**Before:** Ask the children to remind you of possible pitfalls when using written methods. **After:** Check through answers together and troubleshoot difficulties.	10	139

Activity name	Learning objectives	Content of homework	Managing the homework	All New 100 Maths Lessons Year 5	
				NNS	**Page**
How much?	• **Use all four operations to solve simple word problems involving numbers and quantities** based on 'real life', money and measures.	**Maths homework** Word problems.	**Before:** Ask the children to remind you of the order of working through word problems. **After:** Assess the methods used.	**10**	**140**
Zob's space journey	• Choose and use appropriate number operations to solve problems, and appropriate ways of calculating: mental, mental with jottings, written methods, calculator.	**Puzzles to do at home** Zob's space exploration.	**Before:** Explain how fuel consumption is measured. **After:** Compare results and methods of calculation.	**10**	**142**
Multiple sort	• Recognise multiples of 6, 7, 8, 9 up to the tenth multiple.	**Maths to share** Times-table game.	**Before:** Explain the rules and tell the children that some numbers are in more than one times-table. They must identify at least one of them. **After:** Invite the children to discuss the more difficult numbers. Are there any times-tables they need to relearn?	**11**	**148**
Painting by multiples	• Recognise multiples of 6, 7, 8, 9 up to the tenth multiple. • Know and apply tests of divisibility of 2, 4, 5, 10.	**Puzzles to do at home** Children colour the picture according to given multiples.	**Before:** Say that the picture is symmetrical and ask the children to remind you what this means. **After:** Display the pictures as attractive evidence of their learning.	**11**	**149**

Name Date

Where is the hottest place?

- Use either the temperature chart below or a chart of temperatures around the world or in Britain from a newspaper.

Temperatures in °C

Amsterdam	13	Helsinki	–1
Beijing	8	London	13
Berlin	10	Los Angeles	18
Bombay	34	Malta	23
Cairo	24	Montreal	0
Cardiff	11	Moscow	–2
Corfu	20	Nairobi	20
Dublin	11	New York	6
Edinburgh	10	Oslo	4
Florence	21	Tel Aviv	25
Gibraltar	22	Toronto	5
Guernsey	15	Vienna	6

- Write all the temperatures in ascending order, using the < and = symbols.

- Now write some sentences that compare the temperatures of different places. Write on the back of this sheet. Use words and then symbols. For example:

Helsinki is cold, but Moscow is slightly colder. $-2 < -1$

Corfu is cooler than Malta, which is much hotter than Vienna. $20 < 23 > 6$

Dear Helper

This activity helps your child to think about positive and negative numbers on a scale. Remind your child that the bigger a negative number is, the colder the temperature is. Make sure they understand that < means 'less than', > means 'more than'. An interesting spin-off from this activity would be to get an atlas and find these places, then think about why they are hotter or colder than other places.

Name Date

Tables builder

- Complete these times-tables. You should know these already.

10×	**2×**	**3×**	**4×**
1 × 10 = 10	1 × 2 = 2	1 × 3 = 3	1 × 4 = 4
2 × 10 =	2 × 2 =	2 × 3 =	2 × 4 =
3 × 10 =	3 × 2 =	3 × 3 =	3 × 4 =
4 × 10 =	4 × 2 =	4 × 3 =	4 × 4 =
5 × 10 =	5 × 2 =	5 × 3 =	5 × 4 =
6 × 10 =	6 × 2 =	6 × 3 =	6 × 4 =
7 × 10 =	7 × 2 =	7 × 3 =	7 × 4 =
8 × 10 =	8 × 2 =	8 × 3 =	8 × 4 =
9 × 10 =	9 × 2 =	9 × 3 =	9 × 4 =
10 × 10 =	10 × 2 =	10 × 3 =	10 × 4 =

- Now use those times-tables to build up the following less well-known times tables.

12× = 10× + 2×	**13**× = 10× + 3×	**14**× = 10× + 4×	**15**× = 10× + 5×
1 × 12 =	1 × 13 =	1 × 14 =	1 × 15 =
2 × 12 =	2 × 13 =	2 × 14 =	2 × 15 =
3 × 12 =	3 × 13 =	3 × 14 =	3 × 15 =
4 × 12 =	4 × 13 =	4 × 14 =	4 × 15 =
5 × 12 =	5 × 13 =	5 × 14 =	5 × 15 =
6 × 12 =	6 × 13 =	6 × 14 =	6 × 15 =
7 × 12 =	7 × 13 =	7 × 14 =	7 × 15 =
8 × 12 =	8 × 13 =	8 × 14 =	8 × 15 =
9 × 12 =	9 × 13 =	9 × 14 =	9 × 15 =
10 × 12 =	10 × 13 =	10 × 14 =	10 × 15 =

Dear Helper

This is an exercise in building up times-tables knowledge from multiplication facts that your child already knows. If your child knows 2 × 10 and 2 × 4, then they can find 2 × 14 by adding these two results together. Encourage your child to work in a methodical way. If you feel a further challenge would be helpful, ask them to build the 21 or 22 times-table.

Name Date

Use what you know

- Use the two multiplication strategies that we have learned at school this week – finding factors and using near multiples of 10, then adjusting – to solve the following problems.

- Find the factors (remember, there may be more than one combination of factors you could try!)

For example, $12 \times 20 =$
$(6 \times 2) \times (2 \times 10) =$
$((2 \times 2) \times 6) \times 10 =$
$(4 \times 6) \times 10 =$
$24 \times 10 = 240$

12 × 18	20 × 17
24 × 15	25 × 24

- Use near multiples of 10

For example, $24 \times 21 =$
just over $24 \times 20 =$
$(24 \times 2) \times 10 = 480$
and $480 + (1 \times 24) = 504$

18 × 21	18 × 19
26 × 21	26 × 19

Dear Helper
These problems help your child to use multiplication skills learned at school. Encourage your child to explain the strategies to you – this will help their understanding, and also help yours! A worked example of each strategy has been included to remind your child how to do it. If they work out these problems easily, you could stretch their skills further by challenging them to multiply by 31, 29, 41 or 39. This will involve using both strategies to find the answer.

Name Date

Sort them out

- Fill in this grid, using the numbers 1–16 only once each. Each number must follow the rules for the row and the column that it belongs to. One number has been done for you.

1, 2, 3, 4, 5, 6, 7, 8, 9, 10, 11, 12, 13, 14, 15,16

	even number	factor of 24	<8	odd number
square number	16			
>6				
multiple of 3				
<12				

Dear Helper
This puzzle helps your child to solve problems including factors, multiples and square numbers. It needs to be approached methodically, as several numbers might fit in more than one cell. Your child needs to find the cells that have only one possible answer, and work carefully from there. There are some obvious starting points – for example, 1 and 9 are the only square numbers in the list that are odd, and only one of them is less than 8. If your child has found this puzzle easy, challenge them to invent a similar puzzle using different sorting criteria. Can you solve it?

Name Date

Charlie's chocolate chips

- Charlie had between 30 and 50 chocolate chips.
  - He counted the chocolate chips in 4s. There were two left over.
  - He counted them again in 5s. There was one left over.
  - How many chocolate chips did Charlie have? ____________

Dear Helper

This problem tests your child's knowledge of multiples and ability to solve problems. It can be solved by pure trial and error – for example, working through all the multiples of 5 until the answer is found. Alternatively, your child could list all the multiples of 5 and add 1 to each, then list the multiples of 4 and add 2 to each, then look for a number that is common to both lists. A further challenge might be to ask your child to group the same number in 5s and 6s, or in 7s and 9s, with none left over.

Name Date

Fractions and decimals

- Link each fraction to its equivalent decimal with a coloured pencil line.
- Use your knowledge of decimals to do this. Use a calculator for any that you do not know.

$\frac{1}{10}$	0.5
$\frac{4}{10}$	0.2
$\frac{1}{5}$	0.9
$\frac{2}{10}$	0.75
$\frac{90}{100}$	0.33
$\frac{1}{2}$	0.2
$\frac{1}{4}$	0.5
$\frac{3}{4}$	0.7
$\frac{5}{10}$	0.3
$\frac{1}{3}$	0.4
$\frac{30}{100}$	0.1
$\frac{70}{100}$	0.25

Dear Helper

This activity helps your child to remember what decimals are equivalent to some familiar fractions. It is very useful for your child to remember as many of these equivalents as possible, both for working out weights, measures and fractions of numbers and for work on percentages later this year. Challenge your child to see how many of the fraction-decimal pairs shown above they can recall without using the calculator.

Name Date

Ordering masses

- Warning! Ask permission at home before you do this, and make sure an adult is watching you before you handle any containers. Don't touch cleaning materials or other chemicals. Remember to put everything away neatly after you have finished.
- Find eight different packets and jars in your store cupboards that are weighed in grams or kilograms. Put them in order of increasing mass, the lightest first. To do this, you will have to convert them all into the same unit of measure: kilograms (kg). For example, 500g = 0.5kg. Record the masses by drawing and labelling them in this grid.

1	5
2	6
3	7
4	8

Dear Helper

This activity involves looking at different masses (weights) and converting them to a common unit (kilograms or kg). Having a common unit makes the numbers easier to order. If your child is struggling, please do not weigh the items, since the jars, bottles and tins are labelled with the mass of the contents alone. Please do not confuse your child by converting into pounds and ounces! Encourage your child to convert all the masses to grams and then order the items physically before recording them on the grid. As a further challenge, ask your child to estimate the masses of some items in grams and then convert them to kg. Even small masses can be estimated and recorded in this way – for example, 25g = 0.025kg.

Name Date

Looking at lines

- Look around your home (including the garden if you have one) for examples of parallel or perpendicular lines.
- Describe them in this table.

Type of lines	Example

Dear Helper

First establish with your child the difference between perpendicular lines (a pair of lines at right angles to each other) and parallel lines (a pair of lines that are equally spaced apart and will never meet or cross). Then look carefully around your home. Buildings have to be designed with perpendicular and parallel lines for stability. As a further challenge, ask your child to look for perpendicular lines that do not extend from a straight line but from a curved surface (for example, strings in a tennis racquet).

Name Date

Finding areas

- Find the area of these shapes. Look carefully at the units of measurement: you will need to convert some of them.

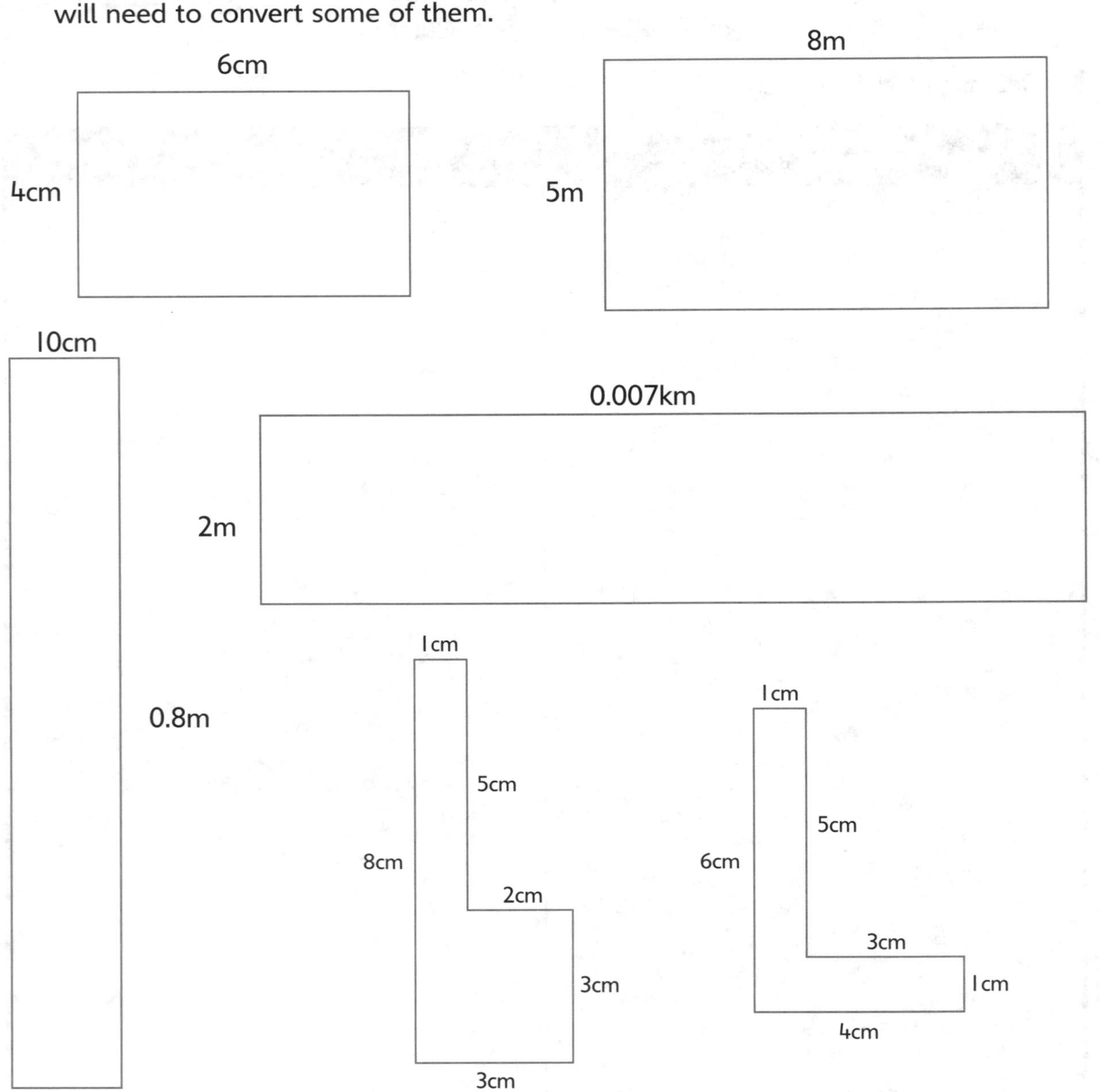

Dear Helper

The area of a square or rectangle can be found by multiplying its length and its breadth (width), but this is only possible if the two measurements are in the same unit of measure (such as cm or m). If they are not, then one value must be changed by multiplying or dividing so that they are both in a common unit. It will help if your child remembers that there are 100cm in a metre and 1000m in a kilometre. If necessary, help your child to see that a composite shape such as an 'L' shape can be divided up into two or more rectangles; they can find the area of each rectangle, then add the areas together. Challenge your child to create a shape made up of rectangles and squares, then calculate the area.

Name Date

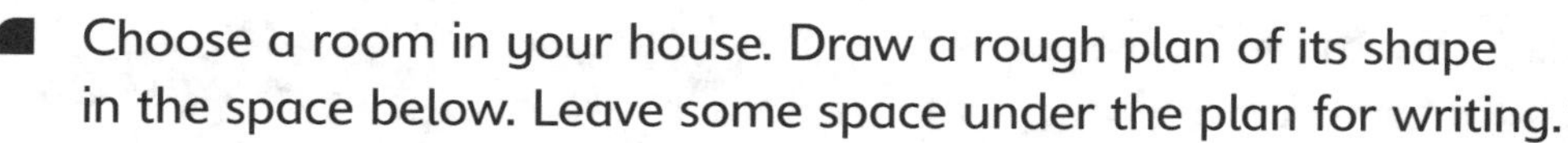

Living space

- Choose a room in your house. Draw a rough plan of its shape in the space below. Leave some space under the plan for writing.
- Divide the shape you have drawn into squares or rectangles. Measure the length and breadth of each rectangle and mark these on your plan. It may be helpful to round the numbers to the nearest 10cm for easier multiplication.
- Now use the length × breadth formula to find the area of each rectangle. Mark the area of each section on your plan. Use these to calculate the total floor area of your room. Attempt the calculation without a calculator, and show your working here. You can then check your answer with a calculator!

Dear Helper

Your help will be essential with this exercise. Your child may find the plan of a room difficult to visualise, and you can help by indicating one wall at a time and pointing out any variations (such as alcoves). Look at the plan and help your child to divide it up into rectangles of various sizes. Remind them that the formula for finding area only applies to squares and rectangles. Help your child to measure one section at a time and label its length and breadth on the plan. Apply the formula to find the area of each section, then add these areas together to find the total floor area of the room. Challenge your child to draw a ground plan of one floor of your home, then calculate the approximate area.

Name Date

Access all areas

- Use newspapers, magazines and the internet (if possible) to research things that are sold by area – that is, sold in cm^2 or m^2 or km^2. Some publications might mention acres or hectares as units of measure. How many different things can you find?
- Collect evidence of these things, such as advertisements. Stick them in the space below to make a display.

Dear Helper

Your child may need some guidance in looking for suitable advertisements. Try the land and property pages of newspapers, catalogues from builders' merchants, adverts from landscape gardeners, aggregate sales in the telephone directory and anything from suppliers of garden and DIY materials. As a challenge, ask your child to compare the prices of floor coverings such as carpets (sold in m^2) and floor tiles (sold in cm^2), converting the units as necessary.

Name Date

Missing data

■ Complete these graphs from the information provided. Answer the questions.

Bar graph to show the number of daily visitors to a website

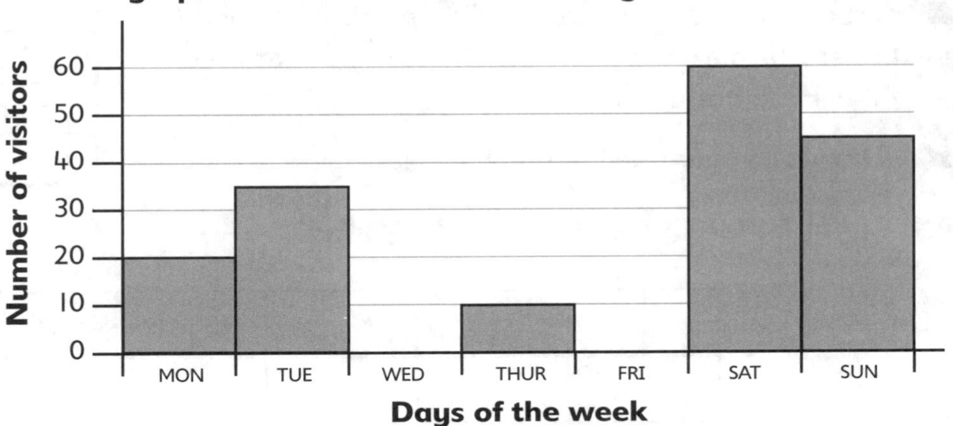

1. There were 35 visitors on Wednesday. Draw the bar to show this.

2. There were 42 visitors on Friday. Show this information on the graph.

3. What was the total number of visitors to the website that week? ____________

Line graph to show the temperature in my garden on a day in July

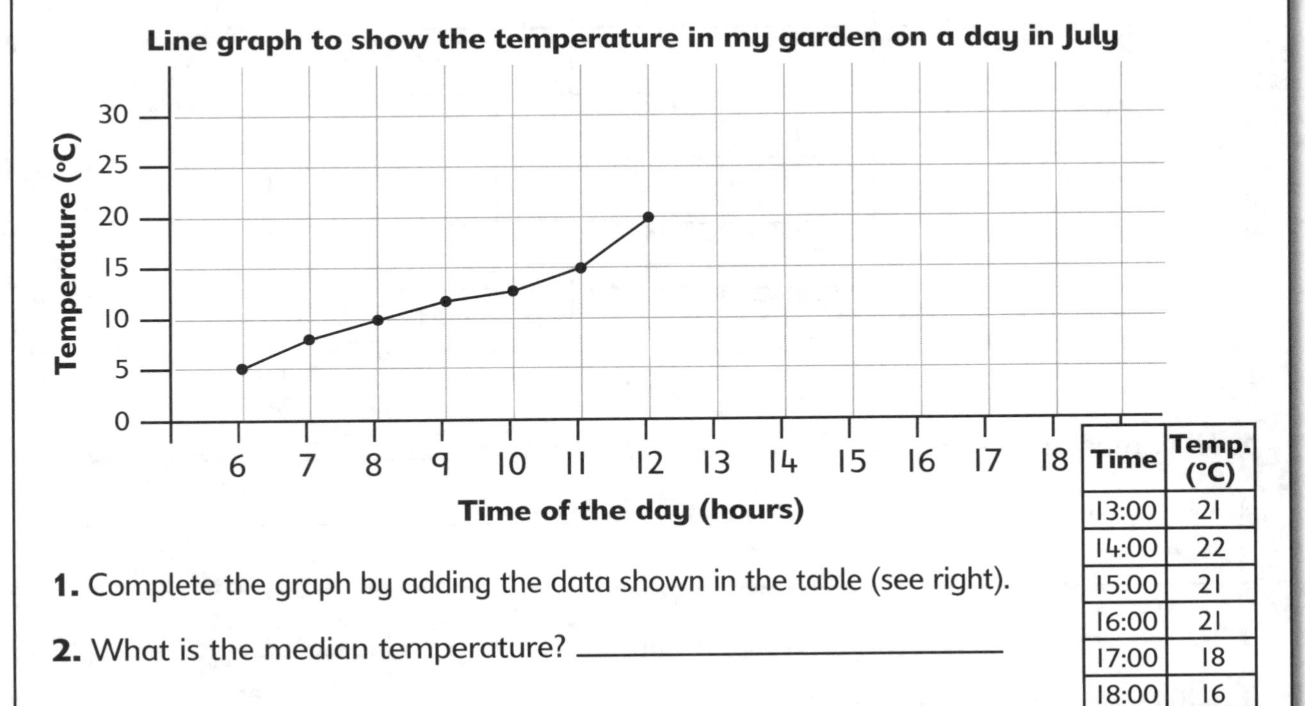

Time	Temp. (°C)
13:00	21
14:00	22
15:00	21
16:00	21
17:00	18
18:00	16

1. Complete the graph by adding the data shown in the table (see right).

2. What is the median temperature? ____________

Dear Helper

This activity will help your child to display data on graphs, and to interpret what the graphs show. Encourage your child to look at the scale carefully, especially when recording a value between two marked points on the scale. The median is the middle value when the data are arranged in ascending order. If your child gets stuck, go through the information provided with them step by step.

Name Date

Fruit facts

	Girls	Boys
bananas	12	6
pears	8	9
apples	4	0
satsumas	11	18
grapes	15	17

- A survey asked 100 Year 5 children (50 girls and 50 boys) which fruit they would choose to eat at break time. Here are the results:
- Draw a comparative bar graph to show these results.

A comparative bar graph to show ______________________

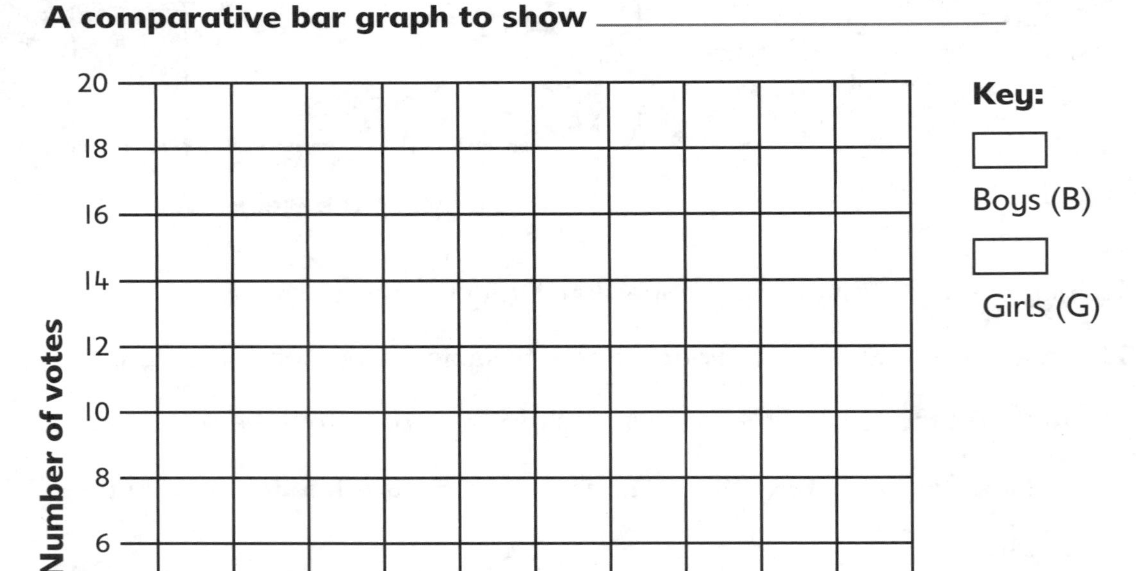

1. How many more boys than girls voted for satsumas? ______________________

2. What was the total number of votes for each fruit? ______________________

____

3. Which was the most popular fruit overall? ______________________

4. Which was the least popular? ______________________

Dear Helper

A comparative bar chart shows two bars in each column, coloured differently and given a key. This allows two sets of results to be compared directly. Encourage your child to understand the difference between finding the total number of votes (both boys and girls) and comparing the two sets of votes. If your child gets stuck, encourage them to go back to the original data and work step by step.

Name Date

Double dice

■ **A game for two people.** You will need two dice.

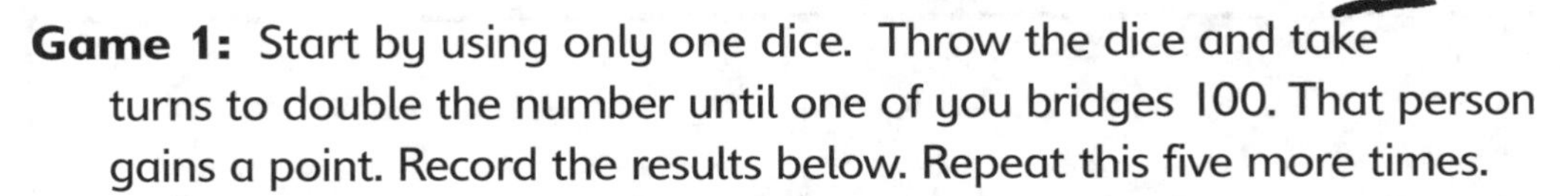

Game 1: Start by using only one dice. Throw the dice and take turns to double the number until one of you bridges 100. That person gains a point. Record the results below. Repeat this five more times.

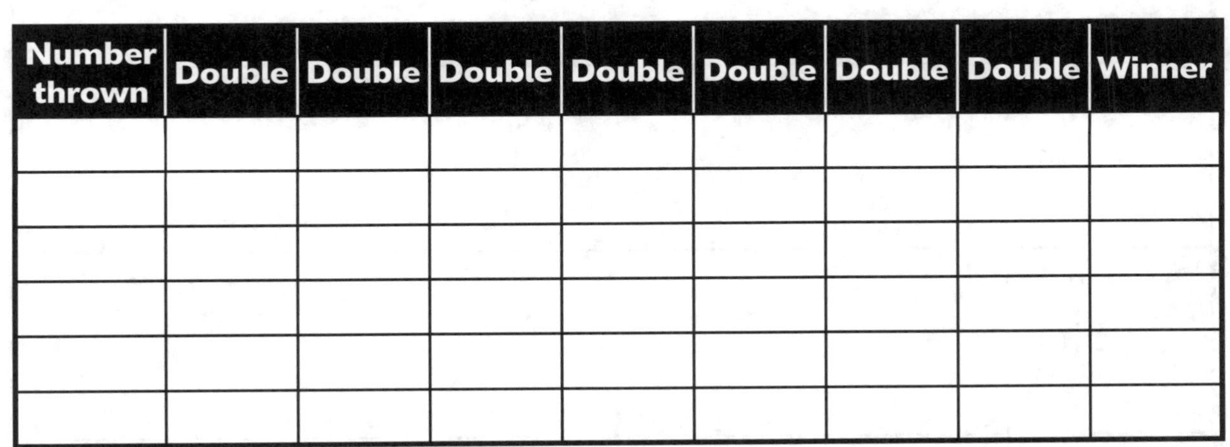

Number thrown	Double	Double	Double	Double	Double	Double	Double	Winner

Game 2: Throw two dice twice. Arrange the digits to make two 2-digit numbers that are quite close together. For example: 6, 4, 2 and 5 can be arranged to make 46 and 52.

- ☐ Use the near double to add the two numbers together, adjusting the answer:

  $46 + 46 = 92$, then $92 + 6 = 98$.

- ☐ Record this addition in the table below.
- ☐ Play four times and add up your totals. The player with the higher score wins.

Numbers	Double	Adjust

Dear Helper
Your child should use these games to practise a variety of strategies for adding. Doubles and near doubles are useful tools for adding mentally or with some informal jottings. You can help your child by encouraging them to learn all of the doubles of numbers to 50, and the corresponding halves. You could do this by making a list and reciting the doubles, then the halves.

Name Date

Calculations page

- Work out these problems, using a written calculation method of your choice.

Problem	Working
421 + 138	
271 + 496	
1143 − 110	
349 − 164	
721 − 348	
289 + 877	
3014 + 1896	

Dear Helper

Please remind your child that they must use a written calculation method. They can choose the best one from the methods they know. They may need help with remembering to 'carry' extra tens or hundreds across to the next column when adding, or with splitting up a tens or hundreds number when subtracting. As an extra challenge, ask your child to add up the answers to the first five calculations, then subtract the answer to the final one.

Name Date

How much?

1. My cat weighs 3.1kg and my dog weighs 5900g. How much is their combined mass?

2. Mrs Jones needs 6.8m of fabric for curtains and a further 320cm of the same material for cushions. How much should she buy?

3. On a round trip to work, Mum drives 8km to drop Dan at his friend's house and pick up my friend Ellie. She then takes Ellie and me 5km to school. Finally she drives a further 8420m to her office. How far does she drive to work each day? She repeats the journey on the way home. How far does she drive each day? How far does she drive in a five-day school week?

4. My dad filled his car up at the petrol station. He bought 37 litres of fuel. The next day, he found that the tank was nearly empty because my brother had borrowed the car. Dad was not pleased about having to buy another 32000ml of fuel. How much fuel had Dad bought in two days? How many litres of fuel had my brother used up?

Dear Helper

This activity helps your child to remember equivalent measures, such as the number of metres in a kilometre. These amounts can be quite difficult to remember, but they are important in real life. You can help your child by doing conversions as they occur in your daily life – for example, when you are shopping or buying petrol. As a challenge, think of some real-life examples of similar problems, and ask your child to write them on the back of this sheet and solve them. For example: *Six bags of crisps cost £1.14. Each bag contains 28g of crisps. What is the total mass of the six bags? How much does one bag cost?*

Name Date

Zob's space journey

- Zob, a space alien from Helios in the Zing and Zang Galaxy, enjoys planet-hopping around the local planet islands.
- Zob's space scooter travels 8km for every litre of fuel.

1 litre of fuel costs 16 orbs.

1. How much fuel does Zob use to get to each of the planet islands and back to Helios?
2. How many orbs does it cost Zob to get to each planet island and back home?

Planet island	Distance from Helios	
Alpha Helio	35km	______
Phillio	41km	______
Zeptra Minor	28km	______
Zeptra Major	14km	______
Qwark	37km	______

Dear Helper

This activity helps your child to work out a problem with more than one step. Your child needs to answer question 1 in order to go on and answer question 2. You may need to help your child understand that the first task is to calculate how many litres of fuel Zob needs for each return journey. Assume that you can only buy whole litres, so Zob may have to buy a little more than he/she/it actually needs. Then your child can calculate the cost of each return journey in orbs.

Name Date

Multiple sort

- **This is a game for two to four players.**
  - Carefully cut out the number cards below. Shuffle the cards and place them face down. Take turns to pick one card up.
  - The first player to call out a times-table and a multiplication fact that the number belongs to wins the card. For example: '81 is in the 9 times table, 9 × 9 is 81'or '72 is in the 8 (or 9) times table, 8 × 9 = 72'.
- The player with the most cards at the end is the winner.

81	12	30	48	72
32	49	42	21	35
18	36	56	64	63
27	40	90	28	16

Dear Helper
This activity encourages your child to recall facts from the 6, 7, 8 and 9 times-tables. It can, of course, be extended to include the other factors of the numbers on the cards. If your child is unsure, encourage them by reciting the appropriate tables together. However, this would be a sign that they needed to spend time learning the multiplication facts so that they could recall them easily.

Name Date

Painting by multiples

■ Colour all the multiples of:

6 red **7** blue **8** yellow **9** purple **10** orange

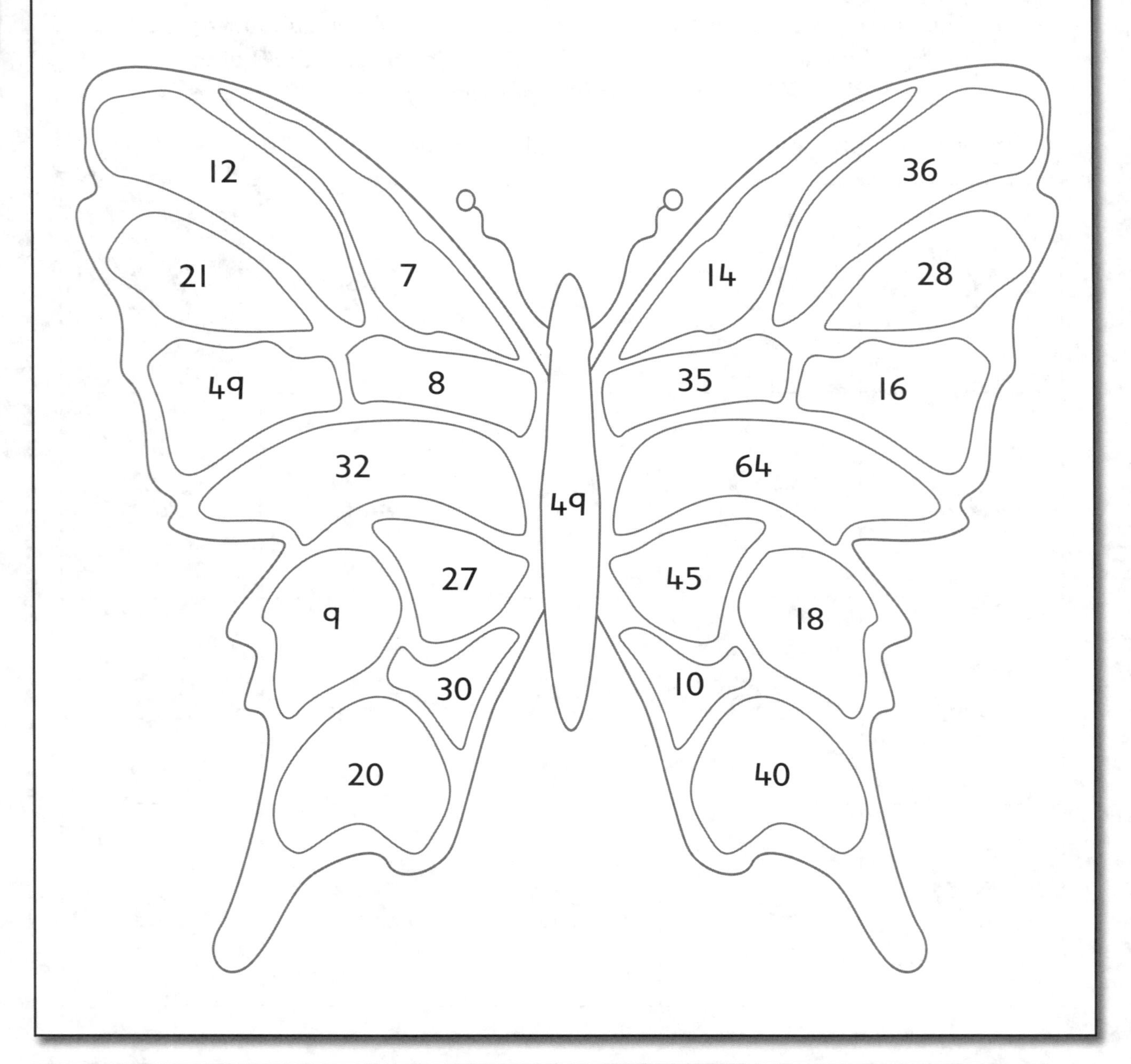

Dear Helper

This is a fun activity that will reinforce your child's knowledge of multiples and their ability to decide whether a given number is divisible by another number. If your child finds some of these multiples difficult, suggest that they write out the 6, 7, 8, 9 and 10 times tables to help them. Your child might also enjoy making up a picture puzzle of this kind.

Teacher's notes

Activity name	Learning objectives	Content of homework	Managing the homework	All New 100 Maths Lessons Year 5	
				NNS	Page
Number search	• Round any integer up to 10,000 to the nearest 10, 100 or 1000.	**Puzzles to do at home** Children look for lines of four numbers that can be rounded to the same whole 10 or 100.	**Before:** Ask the children to remind you of the rule that they created to assist them with rounding numbers. **After:** Invite the children to share their results.	1	154
Tem-perature differences	• Calculate a temperature rise or fall across 0°C.	**Maths homework** Children order temperatures and find differences between them.	**Before:** Remind the children of how we can count through zero when finding changes in temperature involving negative numbers. **After:** Invite someone who researched the challenge to tell the class the coldest place they discovered.	1	156
What's left?	• Begin to express a quotient as a fraction, or as a decimal when dividing a whole number by 2, 4, 5, or 10, or when dividing £ and pence.	**Maths homework** Mixed word and number questions to practise division with decimal and fraction remainders.	**Before:** Ask the children to remind you of the system they follow to answer word problems. **After:** Share some results together to try to spot difficulties.	2	159
More times	**• Extend written methods to long multiplication of TU by TU.**	**Maths homework** Long multiplication practice including decimals.	**Before:** Invite the children to tell you some rules for long multiplications and possible errors to avoid. **After:** Share answers and spot problems.	3	164
Fair play	**• Use all four operations to solve simple word problems involving numbers and money.**	**Maths to share** Calculations based on a visit to a fair. Children make decisions about calculations and methods.	**Before:** Discuss with the children possible ways of solving this problem. **After:** Compare the 'best value' and encourage the children to discuss reasons for their decisions.	3	167
Three of a kind	• Relate fractions to their decimal representations: that is, recognise the equivalence between decimal and fraction forms.	**Maths homework** Children work out fractions, decimals and percentage equivalents.	**Before:** Invite the children to explain the equivalents they are comfortable with using from the class lesson. **After:** Have a class remembering time and ask the children if they have committed to memory any new equivalents.	4	170

Teacher's notes

Activity name	Learning objectives	Content of homework	Managing the homework	All New 100 Maths Lessons Year 5	
				NNS	Page
Special offers	● Begin to understand percentage as the number of parts in every 100 and find simple percentages of small whole-number quantities.	**Maths to share** Children compare offers made by various shops and decide which offers the best deal.	**Before:** Discuss how advertisements aim to encourage people to think that they are getting a good deal. **After:** Discuss the children's findings and investigate the extension activity.	4	172
A collection of parts	● Begin to understand percentage as the number of parts in every 100 and find simple percentages of small whole-number quantities.	**Puzzles to do at home** Children collect examples of everyday use of percentages and fractions, eg in adverts, newspaper headlines etc. They create a display or collage.	**Before:** Invite the children to suggest places where they have observed references to fractions, decimals and percentages in real life. **After:** Compare findings and create a display.	4	174
Ratio problems	● Solve simple problems using ideas of ratio and proportion.	**Maths homework** Children draw ratio pictures to match information.	**Before:** Remind the children how they drew ratios in class. Invite a demonstration. **After:** Share and check results.	5	176
Proportion problems	● Solve simple problems using ideas of ratio and proportion. ● Begin to understand percentages as the number of parts in every 100 and find simple percentages of small whole-number quantities.	**Maths homework** Children answer questions about percentages, ratio and proportion.	**Before:** Invite the children to remind you of the link between percentages and proportion and how to find a fraction of a number. **After:** Share results and invite the children who created some of their own questions to challenge the rest of the class.	5	180
Every graph tells a story	● Solve a problem by representing and interpreting data in tables, charts, graphs and diagrams, including those generated by computer, first where intermediate points have no meaning and then where they may have meaning.	**Maths to share** Children look at a line graph provided, label the axes and tell the story (could be level of noise in a classroom, or filling a bath).	**Before:** Discuss with the children what the line graph could mean and what the x and y axes represent. **After:** Make a display of the suggestion for this graph story.	6	183

Activity name	Learning objectives	Content of homework	Managing the homework	All New 100 Maths Lessons Year 5	
				NNS	Page
Sort it!	• Solve a problem by representing and interpreting data in tables, charts, graphs and diagrams, including those generated by computer, first where intermediate points have no meaning and then where they may have meaning.	**Maths homework** Children answer questions using a Carroll diagram for sorting information.	**Before:** Invite a child to tell you how a Carroll diagram is used. **After:** Share the results of children's own diagrams.	6	187
Reflect on that	• Complete symmetrical patterns with two lines of symmetry at right angles.	**Puzzles to do at home** Children complete a symmetrical pattern.	**Before:** Invite the children to remind you of how a shape or point may be reflected. **After:** Ask the children to swap their patterns with a partner and check the patterns.	8	195
Flip it!	• Recognise where a shape will be after reflection in a mirror line parallel to one side (sides not all parallel or perpendicular to mirror lines).	**Maths homework** Shapes to reflect.	**Before:** Invite the children to tell you how to reflect solid shapes, co-ordinate by co-ordinate. **After:** Ask the children to swap their grids with a partner and check the accuracy of the reflections.	8	197
Translate and reflect	• Recognise where a shape will be after translation. • Recognise where a shape will be after reflection in a mirror line parallel to one side.	**Maths homework** Children create a simple co-ordinate picture, then translate it from one quadrant to another according to a given formula, then reflect it in a horizontal mirror line.	**Before:** Ask the children to explain to you how to translate and reflect a co-ordinate. Tell them they will need to explain to their helpers at home! **After:** Compare and check the patterns created.	9	199
Activities diary	• Use units of time; read time on a 24-hour digital clock and use 24-hour notation.	**Maths to share** Children keep a time diary for given activities. They calculate time spent doing these things in a day.	**Before:** Discuss the activities that the children do in a day. Ask them to estimate how many hours they spend in bed in a week. **After:** Compare the children's findings and use them as a basis for a display.	9	202

Teacher's notes

Activity name	Learning objectives	Content of homework	Managing the homework	All New 100 Maths Lessons Year 5	
				NNS	Page
Currencies around the world	• **Use all four operations to solve simple word problems involving numbers and quantities** based on 'real life', money and measures, including making simple conversions of pounds to foreign currency.	**Maths to share** Children find out which countries use the euro and what the exchange rate is. They investigate other currencies of the world and their exchange rates.	**Before:** Discuss with the class the various sources of information that might prove useful. **After:** Share the children's findings in class discussion time.	10	208
The school barbecue	• Extend written methods to column addition/subtraction of more than two integers less than 10,000; addition or subtraction of a pair of decimal fractions both with one or more decimal places.	**Maths homework** Money questions related to a real-life situation: catering for a barbecue.	**Before:** Discuss with the children the strategies they might use to answer these questions. **After:** Compare answers and invite some children to discuss their methods.	11	214
Colour, add and win	• Use known number facts and place value for mental addition and subtraction.	**Maths to share** Addition and subtraction game.	**Before:** Establish the playing rules and demonstrate using the example on the sheet. **After:** Children swap sheets with a partner and check the calculations.	11	211
Target number game	• Choose and use appropriate number operations and appropriate ways of calculating.	**Maths to share** Target number game, using 2, 6, 7, 4, 12, 21.	**Before:** Explain the rules and have a 'practice run' in class with a different target number. **After:** Compare the scores and invite individuals to share their most inventive calculations.	11	215
Colour me odd or even?	• Make general statements about odd or even numbers, including the outcome of sums and differences.	**Maths homework** Children decide whether answers to given calculations are odd or even and what sort of numbers are generated when various operations are applied.	**Before:** Invite the children to tell you some of the observations they made about calculating with odd and even numbers. **After:** Ask the children to check with a partner that they have the same odd and even answers as each other. Iron out difficulties.	12	220

Number search

- Search for lines of four numbers that would be rounded to the same nearest whole 10 or 100. For example, 16, 18, 19 and 21 would all be rounded to 20.
- Colour or circle the lines of numbers that you find.

16	18	19	21	385
894	141	6	204	401
59	60	61	64	399
112	138	912	249	403
897	913	933	935	226
1001	81	78	77	76
999	206	189	177	179
989	167	888	42	214
1004	188	186	194	187
566	581	612	601	26

Dear Helper
This activity helps your child to round numbers to the nearest 10 or 100. If they find the activity difficult, explain that when we round numbers to the nearest 10, any number ending in 5 or more rounds up rather than down. So 65 rounds up to 70, but 64 rounds down to 60. Likewise, when we round to the nearest 100, any number ending in 50 or more rounds up. So 250 rounds up to 300. If your child finds the lines of numbers easily, challenge them to create a number search of their own, perhaps including decimal numbers.

Name Date

Temperature differences

■ Write these places in order of temperature, the hottest first.

□ You can use the thermometer to help you.

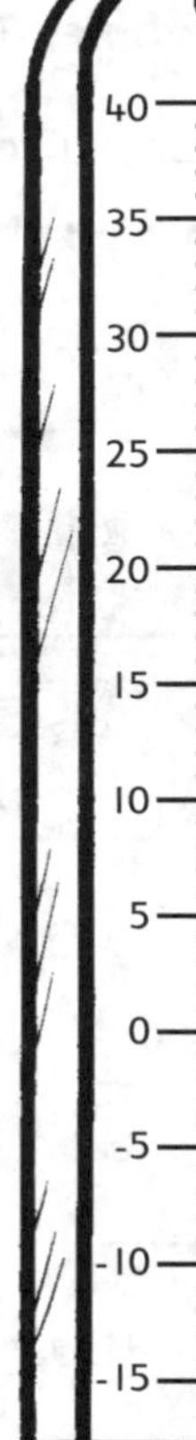

■ Calculate the difference in temperature between:

1. Paris and London ______

2. Helsinki and New York ______

3. Oslo and Paris ______

4. Warsaw and New York ______

Dear Helper

Encourage your child to use the thermometer diagram to help them count through zero when working out differences in temperature. Remind them that the larger the negative number, the colder the temperature will be. A child who finds this difficult may have to count on and back in ones, using the lines shown on the thermometer. Challenge your child to look in newspapers that give information about temperatures around the world. Can they find the greatest difference in temperature?

Name Date

What's left?

- Use your division skills to solve these problems, remembering to convert your remainders to a fraction and then a decimal.

1. Alice measured 267ml of squash and decided that would be enough for four people. How much squash would each person get if it was divided exactly?	**2.** $5\overline{)417}$ $10\overline{)1079}$ $2\overline{)141}$ $4\overline{)145}$
3. Mrs Jones has bought 625cm of wood to make four shelves. How long will each shelf be if the wood is divided exactly?	**4.** I have £167 to spend over a five-day holiday. If I share the money exactly between the five days, how much can I spend on the first day?

Dear Helper
This activity helps your child to understand decimal numbers by looking at division in real-life situations where using decimals makes more sense than using remainders or fractions. We use decimals in most kinds of measures: length, money, capacity and so on. If your child is having difficulties working out the decimal, help them to find the remainder first, then find the fraction (remainder over the number they are dividing by), then relate it to a known equivalent decimal, eg ¼ = 0.25. Challenge your child to answer the following question: *If the answer to a division question is 34.25, what could be the question? Try to think of three different questions.*.

Name Date

More times

- Use the multiplication methods you have learned to solve these written multiplication problems

H	T	U
1	4	6
×	1	3

H	T	U
2	8	1
×	1	5

H	T	U
2	0	7
×	2	6

H	T	U
3	1	8
×	1	4

H	T	U
3	4	2
×	1	5

H	T	U
3	1	8
×	2	3

HTU.th
39.21
× 15

HTU.th
142.63
× 12

HTU.th
35.39
× 21

HTU.th
127.27
× 16

Dear Helper

This activity gives your child practice in long multiplication – that is, written multiplication by a number with more than one digit. The difficulty with the transition from simpler multiplications to long multiplication is the multiplication by the second digit (the tens in this case). If your child is having difficulty, you may need to remind them that if they are multiplying by a tens number, they need to move the answers up the place value line and write a zero in the units column to 'hold' the place value. Please allow your child to show you their method. Please don't teach them a new method. Challenge your child to increase the multiple of each question by 200, for example 342 × 15 becomes 342 × 215. Ask: *What will you have to do to multiply by 'hundreds'? How many place values will you have to hold?*

Name Date

Fair play

- Look at the special offers below.
- Which offer gives the best value for money (the lowest cost per ride)?

- Best value: ______________________________

Because ______________________________

____

- Poorest value: ______________________________

Because ______________________________

____

Dear Helper
This is a 'real-life' problem for your child to solve by calculating. Your child needs to calculate the unit price (the price of each ride) for each offer. Alternatively, they could simply multiply the number of rides by £1.50 each time and compare that with the special offer. So they can choose whether to use division or multiplication – as long as they do so correctly! For children who find this difficult, you may need to convert each problem into a number calculation for them – for example, to find the unit price £4.45 ÷ 3. As a further challenge, talk about the discount offers in supermarkets. Do they always save you money? Why not?

Name Date

Three of a kind

- Draw lines to link the equivalent decimals, fractions and percentages.
  - One trio has been joined up for you.

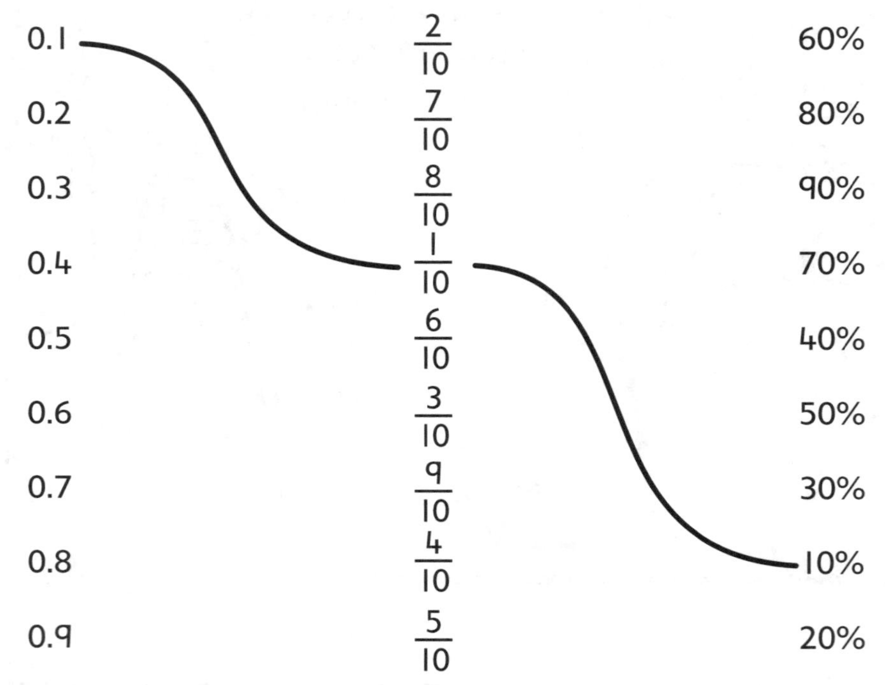

- Draw lines to link the matching amounts.
  - One trio has been joined up for you.

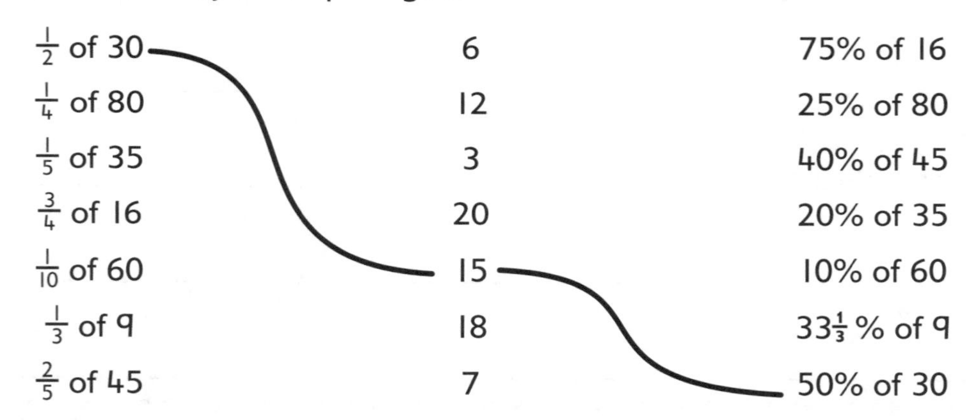

Dear Helper

This activity will help your child to see the links between fractions, decimals and percentages, and show them that they can work out a percentage of an amount by converting it into a fraction (for example, 50% of £10 is $\frac{1}{2}$ of £10 = £5). If your child is struggling, it might be helpful to remind them that the fraction $\frac{1}{10}$ is the same as the decimal 0.1, which is the same as 10%. If your child finds the activity easy, challenge them to think of some other fractions to find the percentage equivalents of – for example, $\frac{1}{4}$ or $\frac{2}{3}$.

Name Date

Special offers

Sam's Sale 20% off everything!

CHEAP & CHEERFUL
25% OFF THE MOST
EXPENSIVE ITEM.

- Look at the advertisements above.
  - Which shop is offering the best reductions? ______________________
  - Explain in words how you know: ______________________

____

- Calculate the cost of buying a pair of gloves and a scarf from each shop.
  - The pre-sale prices were £8.50 for the gloves and £7.25 for the scarf.

Shop	Gloves	Scarf
Sam's Sale		
Bargain Basement		
Cheap & Cheerful		

Dear Helper
This 'real-life' problem helps your child to reason about numbers and make decisions. You can help your child by reminding them of fraction/percentage equivalents such as $\frac{1}{4}$ = 25%. A further challenge might be to increase the number of items bought from each shop and ask your child how expensive the most expensive item has to be in order for 'Cheap & Cheerful' to give better value than 'Bargain Basement'.

Name Date

A collection of parts

- Make a collection of pictures, advertisements, leaflets, newspaper headlines and so on that mention percentages and fractions.
- Display them as a collage, either on the sheet below or on a larger sheet if you prefer.

Dear Helper
Fractions and percentages are often displayed in shops and in advertisements, but many people find them difficult to understand and use. This activity is designed to make fractions and percentages more 'real' to your child. Newspapers and magazines are the best places to start looking. You might like to challenge your child to calculate some of the price reductions being advertised. Or if your child finds the whole concept of fractions and percentages difficult, discuss with them what the advertised price reductions mean.

Name Date

Ratio problems

■ Draw ratio pictures to show the following:

1. There are 12 cats in a ratio of 1:5 ginger to black.

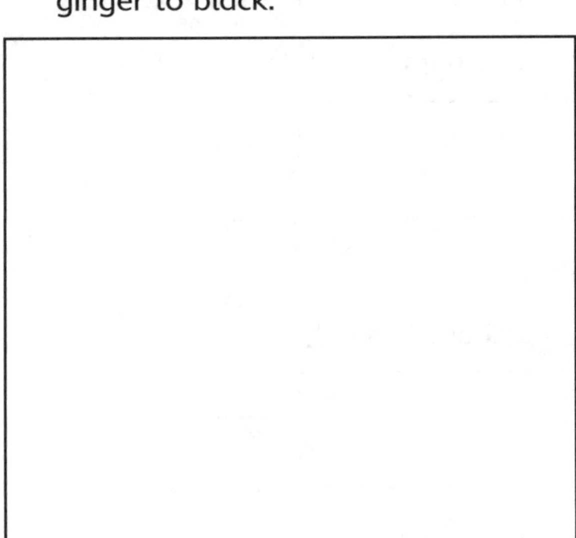

2. There are 21 children in a ratio of 1:2 boys to girls.

3. There are 16 sailing boats in a ratio 3:5 white sails to red sails.

4. There are 15 flowers in a ratio 1:4 blue to yellow.

Dear Helper

This activity helps your child to understand the idea of a ratio. A ratio is the balance between elements that make up a group – for example, a wall might contain one blue brick for every two red bricks. To help your child, remind them that a ratio is like a pattern of beads or cubes that might need to be repeated to make up the total number. A further challenge might be to look for and collect examples of ratios being used in real life.

Name Date

Proportion problems

- Solve these proportion problems.
  - Show your working out.

1. Of 100 people, 5% were unhappy about the amount of litter in their town.

What proportion, and how many people, were quite happy?

2. Of 110 chairs in a school hall, 10% have wobbly legs.

What proportion are safe and sound? How many chairs is that?

3. Eighty per cent of a group of 40 women said they owned a hat.

How many owned a hat? What proportion did not?

4. Ninety-five per cent of a group of 500 children own a pet.

What proportion do not own a pet? How many children are not pet owners?

Dear Helper

This activity helps your child to understand the idea of proportion. A proportion represents a certain number 'out of' a total. Percentages take this a step further, expressing a proportion as a number out of 100 (whatever the actual total number is). For example, the proportion 4 out of 5 is equal to 80%. Encourage your child to express these proportions in their simplest form. For example, 80% = 80/100 = 8/10 = 4/5. If your child is finding these difficult, remind them that percentages can be broken down into 'lots of 10%'. For example, to find 10% of a number we divide that number by 10, so 10% of 50 is 5. We can use this knowledge to find 20% (double it =10) or 5% (halve it = 2.5). Challenge your child to make up some more proportion questions to share at school.

Name Date

Every graph tells a story

- Look at the line graph below.
- What story do you think it is telling?
- Give the graph a title and label the axes.
- Write the story. For example: 'At _____ o'clock ________________ happened.'

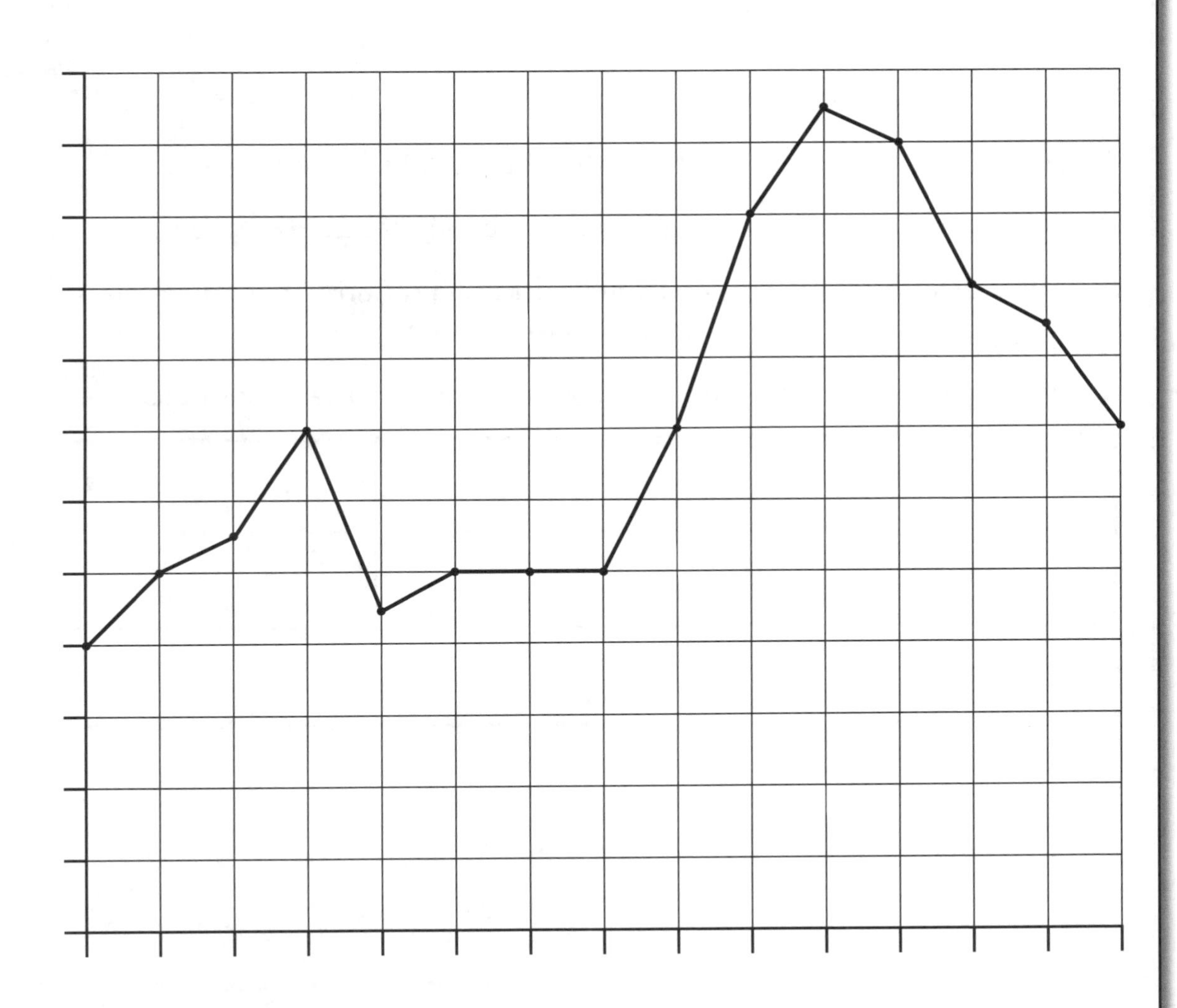

Dear Helper
This graph gives your child an opportunity to think imaginatively. There are no 'right' or 'wrong' answers. Encourage your child to be inventive.

Name Date

Sort it!

- Use the information in this Carroll diagram to answer the questions below.

	Trousers that are jeans	Trousers that are not jeans
Blue	67	54
Not blue	37	48

1. How many pairs of trousers are blue? ______________
2. How many are not blue? ______________
3. How many more jeans are there than other kinds of trousers? ______________
4. How many pairs of trousers are there altogether? ______________

- Think of some items that you could sort using a Carroll diagram. You could use colours, foods, animals or anything else you like.
- Write some questions to go with your diagram, on the back of this sheet.

Dear Helper
This activity helps your child to use Carroll diagrams. A Carroll diagram sorts related items into groups. The numbers in the diagram above show how many pairs of trousers belong under each pair of headings. If your child finds it difficult to think of headings for their own diagram, suggest ideas such as 'Girl bands, boy bands, bands with fewer than four people, bands with four or more people'. Then they can fill in the names of bands that fit the given categories. Challenge your child to think of a diagram using numbers.

Name Date

Reflect on that

- Complete the symmetrical pattern below by reflecting the shapes in all mirror lines.

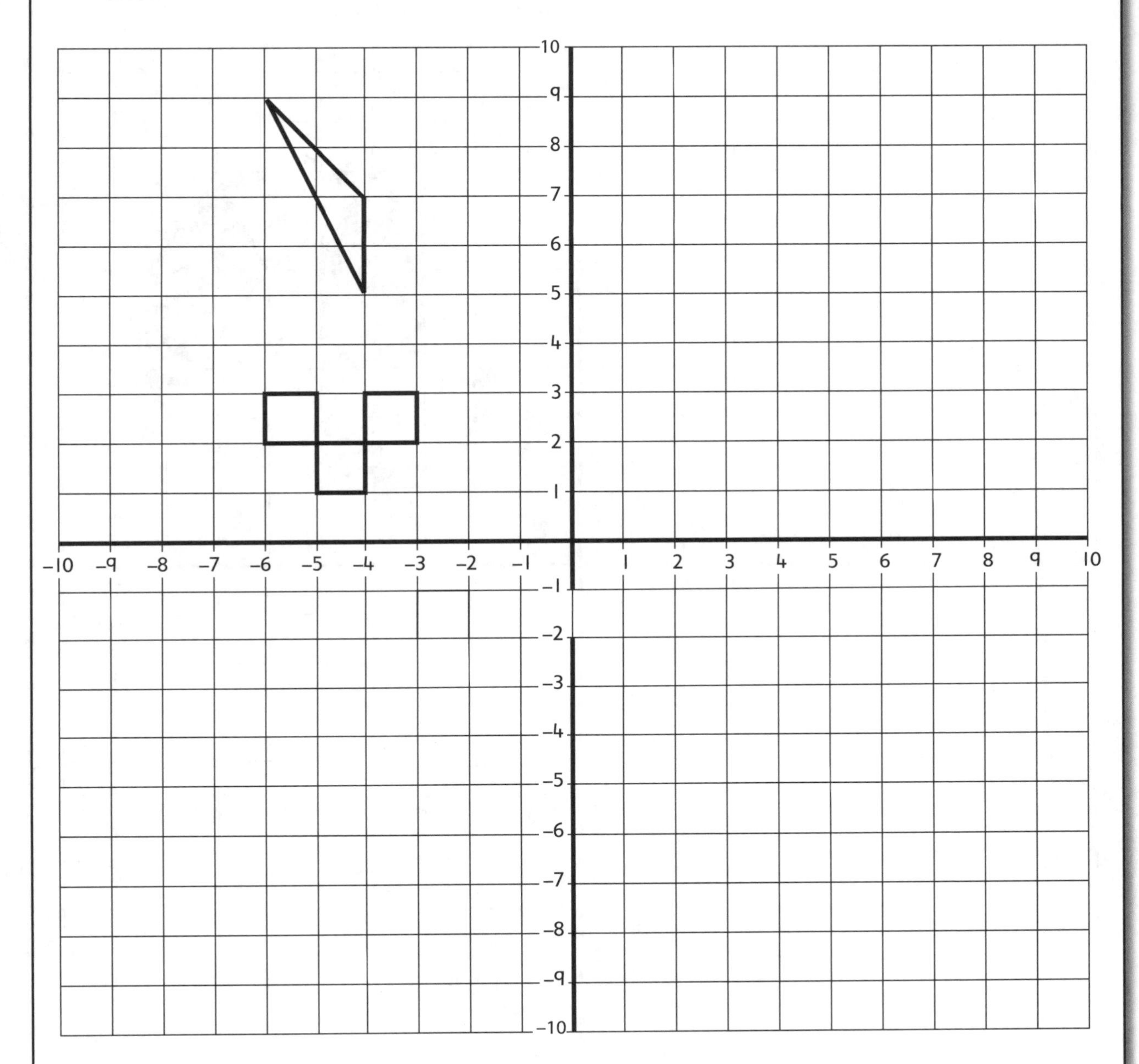

Dear Helper
The important thing to remember with reflecting shapes is that they 'flip over' when reflected so it is sometimes necessary to count the number of squares from each point or corner as shown. Don't forget to reflect the reflection in order to complete a symmetrical pattern in all four quadrants. A further challenge might be to encourage your child to create their own pattern.

Name Date

Flip it!

- Reflect the shapes in both mirror lines.
- Remember to number each reflected point A1, B1, C1, A2, B2, C2 and so on.

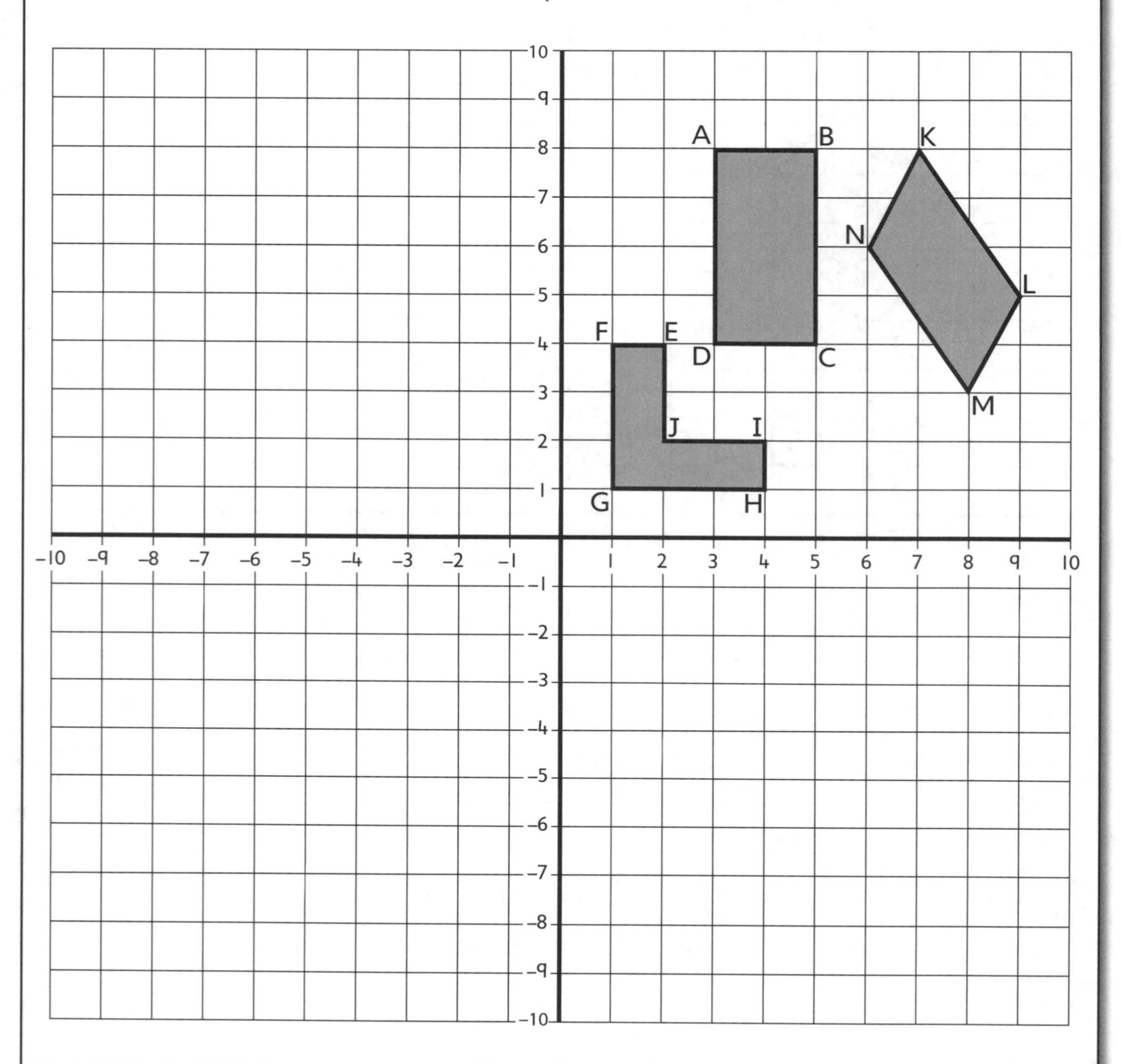

Dear Helper
This exercise requires children to reflect each point separately and then join them up. To reflect a point your child needs to count the number of squares up to the mirror line and the same number away again on the other side of the mirror line. Each shape will invert or 'flip over' as it crosses the mirror line. A further challenge might be to draw a new set of axes on the back of this sheet and draw additional shapes to reflect.

Name Date

Translate and reflect

- Use the co-ordinates below to create a simple picture.
- Translate it according to the formula (x – 8, y) and then reflect the new image in the horizontal mirror line (x axis).

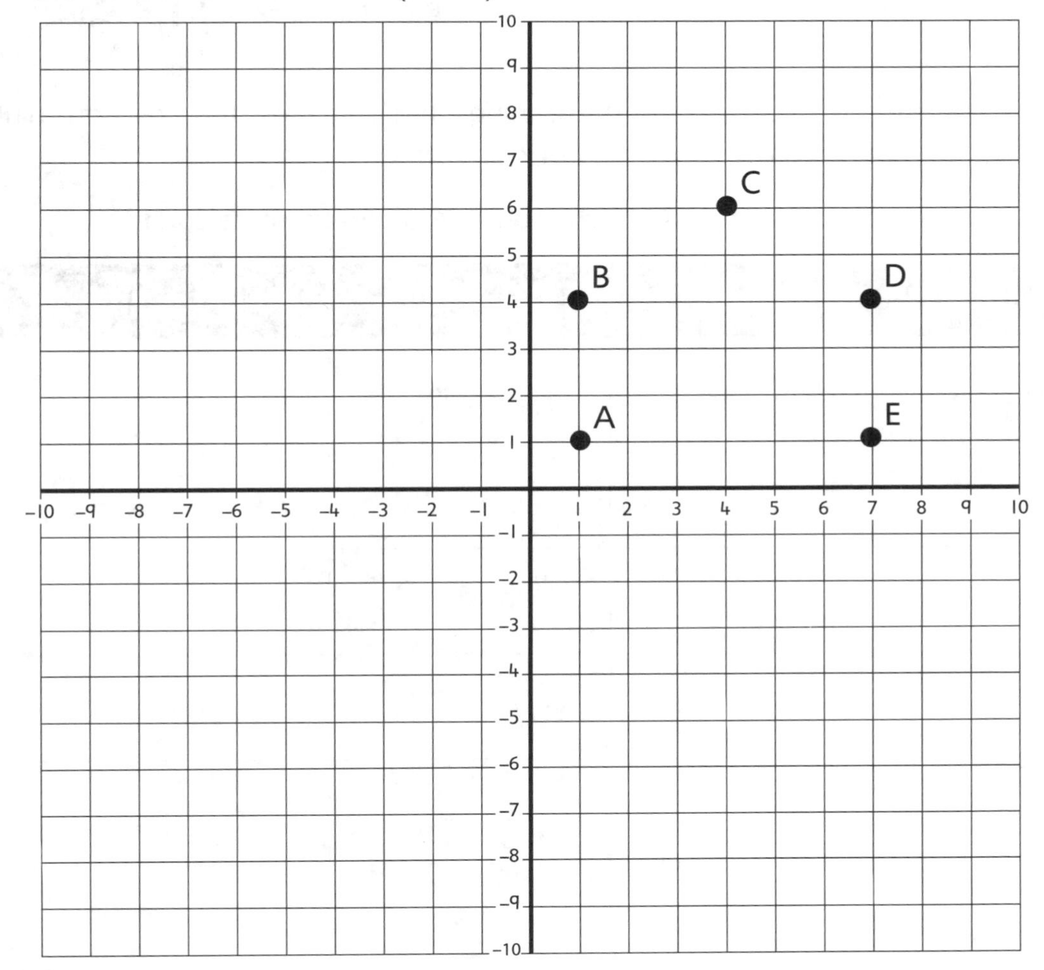

- Join all the points.
- Use the back of this sheet to calculate the new translated shape co-ordinates.

Dear Helper

Your child needs to be reminded that a translation will move points or shapes along, while reflections will invert them on the opposite side of the mirror line. To translate a shape, the co-ordinates (x, y) have a number added or subtracted, so a co-ordinate (2, 4), when a formula such as (x – 6, y – 4) is applied, would become (–4, 0). If your child finds the translation formula difficult, help them by writing out the co-ordinates and then applying the formula together (ie take 8 away from the x number but leave the y number as it is). This will give you the new co-ordinates for the translated shape. Children can use the axis as a number line to help them calculate negative numbers when drawing the reflection. Challenge your child to create their own co-ordinates and formula to translate and reflect shapes.

Name Date

Activities diary

- Keep a diary for 24 hours of the activities given below.
  - Use the recording chart to help.
  - Remember that you may do some things more than once a day.

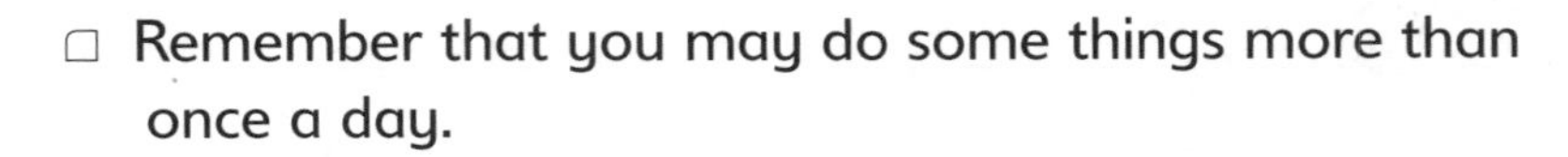

- Calculate the time you spent doing these things in a day. How long do you think you would spend on them over a week or a month or a year?
- Choose your own activities to add to the table. You can use a calculator.

Activity	Time	Time spent	Total for 24 hours
Playing football	11:15 – 12:10	55 mins	
Sleeping			
Eating			
Washing/bathing			
Exercising			
Watching TV/ using computer			

Dear Helper
This is an exercise in calculating times using the 24-hour clock. Remind your child that pm times are the second set of 12 hours in 24, so 1.30pm is written as 13:30. It is an interesting exercise to find out what proportion of our lives we spend sleeping or eating! Some children may need support with the calculating, remembering that there are 60 minutes to the next hour. Encourage them to 'count on' in units of five minutes up to the next hour and then count on in hours.

Name Date

Currencies around the world

- Find out more about different currencies around the world.
- List the countries and currencies you find in the table below.

Country	Currency	Exchange rate

- How many countries in Europe use the euro? List them in the box below.

- If you received £5.00 pocket money, how much would this be in...

US dollars:	
Yen:	
Euros:	
Other:	

Dear Helper

You will find information about currencies and exchange rates in newspapers, atlases, Teletext and on the internet. You may help your child by using a calculator for the conversions. Some children may find the conversions difficult. It may help to remind them about ratio: *For every pound I get* ____. This will then need to be multiplied by 5 to make the equivalent of £5. A further challenge might be to discover some more obscure currencies to convert.

Name Date

The school barbecue

- The school PTA is organising a school barbecue.
- They need to calculate how much food to buy, how much it will cost, and how much to charge for each item to ensure they make a profit.

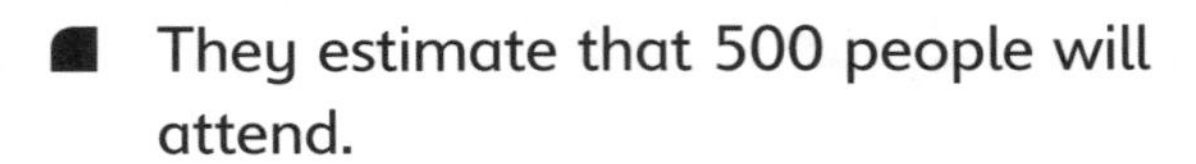

- They estimate that 500 people will attend.
- Use the information in the box (right) to answer the questions below.

500 rolls cost £50.00
500 sausages cost £118.25
500 burgers cost £106.79
500 burger buns cost £50.00
10 bottles ketchup cost £32.60
20 bottles squash cost £48.00

1. How much will 500 hot dogs cost?

____

2. How much will 500 burgers in buns cost?

____

3. How much will 500 burgers in buns and 500 hot dogs cost altogether?

____

4. Add on the cost of the squash and ketchup. What is the grand total spent?

____

5. If they charge each person £3.00 they will take £1500. How much profit will be made?

____

Dear Helper

Please encourage your child to read the questions carefully and to add the numbers in pairs as asked. Do not be tempted to add the whole list as a shopping list since it does not take into account two lots of rolls for sausages and burgers. Encourage your child to use a written method of subtraction. Please do not use a calculator. If your child is struggling, it might help to convert the word problem into a calculation (some children have difficulty recognising which operation to use, ×, ÷, – or +). Write the calculations beside the written questions. Once your child is confident with the task, challenge them to plan their own event and price each item. If available, the data can be entered into a spreadsheet program such as Microsoft Excel, which allows you to change unit costs and recalculate.

Name Date

Colour, add and win

- You need some coloured pencils and a dice.
- Take it in turns to throw the dice three times.
- You must decide whether to add or subtract the numbers in order to colour one of the answer sections in the picture.
- Record your chosen sum below. The first example has been done for you.

Player 1	Player 2
6 + 5 – 2 = 9	6 + 6 + 1 = 13

Dear Helper
Encourage your child to be inventive with their mental calculations to achieve all the numbers, for example, 4 + 4 – 6 = 2. Children who have real difficulty calculating with both operations may find that having 18 counters helps, particularly when combining addition and subtraction in inventive ways in order to make a tricky number. As a challenge, ask your child to draw their own version of the pictures but number them with a selection of numbers from 12 to 108. They throw the dice three times and use any operation in any order to make the target numbers.

Name Date

Target number game

- Carefully cut out the number cards below.
- Turn them face up.
- Use any of the numbers once and any operation to make the target numbers shown in the table.
- Record the calculation you used.

□ Speed is important because the first person to make their target number gets a point. Two points may be awarded for a more complex calculation using all four operations.

Player 1 TARGET	Calculation	Player 2 TARGET	Calculation
11		11	
5		5	
77		77	
18		18	
20		20	
52		52	

2	6	7	4	12	21

Dear Helper
Remind your child that all four operations means +, –, ÷ and ×. They may use any or all of them in one calculation. Children who find multiplication and division difficult could see how many of the numbers can be made simply by adding and subtracting. Alternatively, the person who gets closest to the given numbers could be the winner, using whichever operations they feel confident with. A further challenge might be to make a new set of number cards using more challenging numbers such as 17 and 41, but keep the same target numbers.

Name Date

Colour me odd or even?

■ Colour all the sections that give an even answer one colour and the sections that give an odd number a second colour.

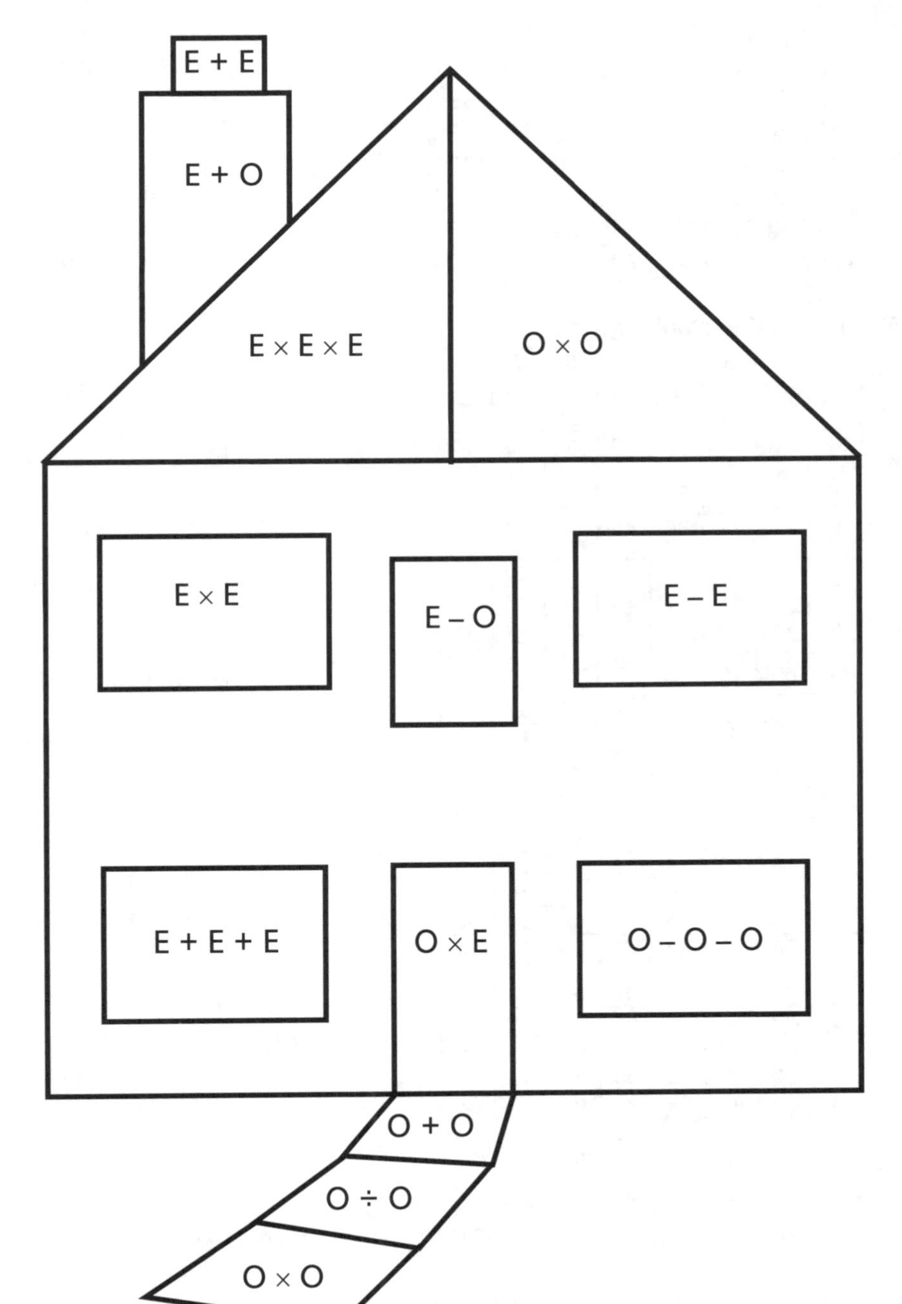

Colour key:

☐ = Odd (O)

☐ = Even (E)

Dear Helper

Certain patterns emerge when calculating with odd and even numbers. If your child is in any doubt, try a couple of examples using numbers to help you decide whether the answer will be odd or even. Challenge your child to create their own picture and odd and even questions.

Answer sheet

Autumn term

P13 Investigating place value Two digits: 28, 82; 67, 76; three digits: 459, 495, 549, 594, 945, 954; 168, 186, 618, 681, 816, 861; four digits: 3578, 3587, 3758, 3785, 3857, 3875, 5378, 5387, 5738, 5783, 5837, 5873, 7358, 7385, 7538, 7583, 7835, 7853, 8357, 8375, 8537, 8573, 8735, 8753; 0347, 0374, 0437, 0473, 0734, 0743, 3047, 3074, 3407, 3470, 3704, 3740, 4037, 4073, 4307, 4370, 4703, 4730, 7034, 7043, 7304, 7340, 7403, 7430.

P15 Times-table challenge

×	2	3	4	5	6	7	8
2	4	6	8	10	12	14	16
4	8	12	16	20	24	28	32
8	16	24	32	40	48	56	64
3	6	9	12	15	18	21	24
6	12	18	24	30	36	42	48
9	18	27	36	45	54	63	72

×	3	4	5	6	7	8	9
4	12	16	20	24	28	32	36
5	15	20	25	30	35	40	45
9	27	36	45	54	63	72	81
3	9	12	15	18	21	24	27
7	21	28	35	42	49	56	63
2	6	8	10	12	14	16	18

×	4	5	6	7	8	9	10
2	8	10	12	14	16	18	20
3	12	15	18	21	24	27	30
4	16	20	24	28	32	36	40
5	20	25	30	35	40	45	50
6	24	30	36	42	48	54	60
7	28	35	42	49	56	63	70

x	6	5	7	8	9	3	4
8	48	40	56	64	72	24	32
4	24	20	28	32	36	12	16
5	30	25	35	40	45	15	20
9	54	45	63	72	81	27	36
7	42	35	49	56	63	21	28
6	36	30	42	48	54	18	24

P18 Multiplication and division word problems 1 £4.50, 72p, £10.00, £1.20. **2** 48p, 40p, £1.44, £2.58. **3** £4.80.

P19 Shape fractions Answers may vary, but ensure coloured shapes match linked fractions.

P21 Quantities for a recipe 12 cakes: 100g each of flour, margarine and sugar, 2 eggs, 2 tbsp cocoa, 12 paper cases. 18 cakes: 150g each of flour, margarine and sugar, 3 eggs, 3 tbsp cocoa, 18 paper cases.

P23 Comparing data 1 15°C. **2** 10°C. **3** London 13°C, Athens 28°C. **4** A line graph is used to show how something measurable, such as a person's temperature, changes over a period of time. A bar chart or a bar line graph is used to compare numbers of separate things, such as cars or different-colour eyes.

P25 Sorting triangles Equilateral - three equal sides, three equal angles; isosceles - two sides of equal length, one side different length; scalene has no equal sides; yes.

P26 Perimeter problem Side lengths in metres of possible rectangles: 1, 1, 14, 14; 2, 2, 13, 13; 3, 3, 12, 12; 4, 4, 11, 11; 5, 5, 10, 10; 6, 6, 9, 9; 7, 7, 8, 8. Seven different rectangles.

P27 Weights and measures Jam g; washing powder kg; milk ml/l; fizzy drink ml; flour kg/g; sugar kg; rice kg/g; soup g; tinned tomatoes g; baked beans g.

P31 Take it away 1 242. **2** 413. **3** 1114. **4** 2147. **5** 469. **6** 828. **7a** 1006; **7b** 152.

P32 Magic squares Four facts: centre edge and opposite numbers = 10; diagonal corners add to make 10; corner numbers are even; centre number of each set of three numbers is odd.

P33 Number chains 1 1, 1, 1. **2** 2, 1, 3, 3. **3** 2, 1, 1, 2. **4** 43, 48, 53. **5** 82, 72, 62. **6** -9, -12, -15. **7** 29, 37, 46.

Spring term

P38 Where is the hottest place? -2 < 1 < 0 < 4 < 5 < 6 = 6 < 8 < 10 = 10 < 11 = 11 < 13 = 13 = 13 < 15 < 18 < 20 = 20 < 21 < 22 < 23 < 24 < 25 < 34.

P39 Tables builder Less well-known times-tables: **12×:** 12, 24, 36, 48, 60, 72, 84, 96, 108, 120; **13×:** 13, 26, 39, 52, 65, 78, 91, 104, 117, 130; **14×:** 14, 28, 42, 56, 70, 84, 98, 112, 126, 140; **15×:** 15, 30, 45, 60, 75, 90, 105, 120, 135, 150.

P40 Use what you know 12 × 18 = 216; 20 × 17 = 340; 24 × 15 = 360; 25 × 24 = 600; 18 × 21 = 378; 18 × 19 = 342; 26 × 21 = 546; 26 × 19 = 494.

P41 Sort them out

16	4	1	9
14	8	7	13
6	12	3	15
10	2	5	11

Answer sheet

P42 Charlie's chocolate chips 46.

P43 Fractions and decimals

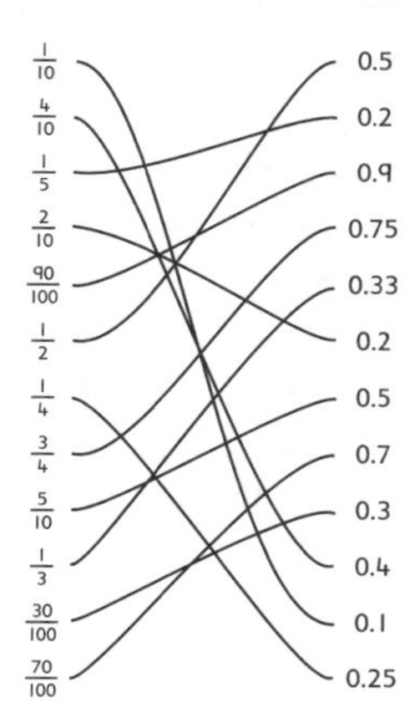

P46 Finding areas 6cm × 4cm = 24cm^2; 5m × 8m = 40m^2; 10cm × 0.8m = 0.08m^2 or 800cm^2; 2m × 0.007km = 14m^2; composite shapes: **a)** 5cm × 1cm = 5cm^2 + 3cm × 3cm = 9cm^2 = 14cm^2; **b)** 5cm × 1cm = 5cm^2 + 4cm × 1cm = 4cm^2 = 9cm^2.

P49 Missing data Total number of visitors = 247; median 16°C.

P50 Fruit facts **1** 7. **2** 18 bananas, 17 pears, 4 apples, 29 satsumas, 32 grapes. **3** grapes. **4** apples.

P52 Calculations page **1** 559. **2** 767. **3** 1033. **4** 185. **5** 373. **6** 1166. **7** 4910.

P53 How much? **1** 9kg. **2** 10m. **3** 21.42km; 42.84km; 214.2km. **4** 69 litres; 32 litres.

P54 Zob's space journey **1** 8.75 litres, 10.25 litres, 7 litres, 3.5 litres, 9.25 litres. **2** 140 orbs, 164 orbs, 112 orbs, 56 orbs, 148 orbs.

Summer term

P61 Number search

16	18	19	21	385
894	141	6	204	401
59	60	61	64	399
112	138	912	249	403
897	913	933	935	226
1001	81	78	77	76
999	206	189	177	179
989	167	888	42	214
1004	188	186	194	187
566	581	612	601	26

P62 Temperature differences 32°C Sydney, 29°C Cairo, 6°C New York, 5°C Paris, 2°C London, -3°C Oslo, -4°C Montreal, -5°C Helsinki, -15°C Warsaw. **1** 3°C. **2** 11°C. **3** 8°C. **4** 21°C.

P63 What's left? **1** 66r3 = 66¾ or 66.75ml. **2** 83r2 = $83\frac{2}{5}$ or 83.4; 107r9 = $107\frac{9}{10}$ or 107.9; 70r1 = 70½ or 70.5; 36r1 = 36¼ or 36.25. **3** 156¼ or 156.25cm. **4** £33.40.

P64 More times 1898; 4215; 5382; 4452; 5130; 7314; 588.15; 1711.56; 743.19; 2036.32.

P65 Fair play Best value: 6 rides for £8.40 representing a saving of 60p on the individual price for each ride. Poorest value: 10 rides for £14.90, giving only a saving of 10p over the individual ride price on 10 rides.

P66 Three of a kind

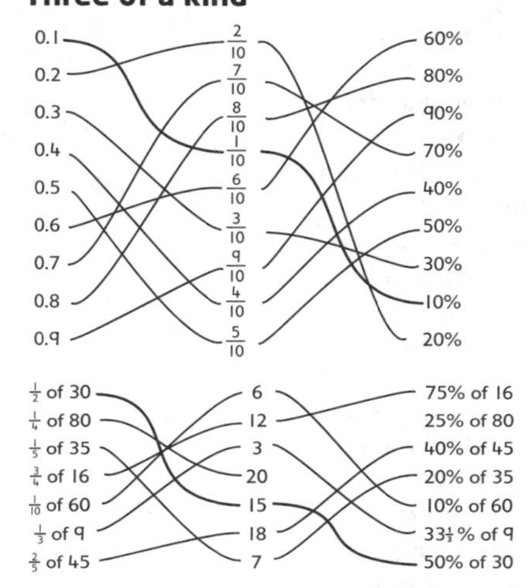

P67 Special offers Best buy: Bargain Basement all prices cut by ¼ (£6.38 for gloves and £5.44 for the scarf). Sam's Sale prices are £6.80 (gloves) and £5.80 (scarf), and Cheap & Cheerful's prices are £6.38 (gloves) and £7.25 (scarf).

P69 Ratio problem Pictures should show:
1 2 ginger cats and 10 black ones.
2 7 boys and 14 girls.
3 6 sailing boats with white sails and 10 with red sails.
4 3 blue flowers and 12 yellow ones.

P70 Proportion problems **1** 95/100 or 95 people were happy. **2** 90/100 = 9/10 or 99 chairs were sound. **3** 32 ladies owned hats or 1/5 did not. **4** 5/100 or 1/20 do not own a pet, that is 25 children.

P72 Sort it! **1** 121. **2** 85. **3** 2. **4** 206.

P78 The school barbecue **1** £168.25. **2** £156.79. **3** £325.04. **4** £405.64. **5** £1094.36.

Year 5 Key objectives

- **a** Multiply and divide any positive integer up to 10,000 by 10 or 100 and understand the effect.
- **b** Order a given set of positive and negative integers.
- **c** Relate fractions to division.
- **d** Use decimal notation for tenths and hundredths.
- **e** Round a number with one or two decimal places to the nearest integer.
- **f** Relate fractions to their decimal representations.
- **g** Calculate mentally a difference such as 8006 – 2993.
- **h** Extend written methods to column addition/subtraction of two integers less than 10,000.
- **i** Know by heart all multiplication facts up to 10 × 10.
- **j** Extend written methods to short multiplication of HTU or U.t by U; long multiplication of TU by TU; short division of HTU by U.
- **k** Use all four operations to solve simple word problems involving numbers and quantities based on 'real life', money and measures (including time).
- **l** Understand area measured in square centimetres (cm^2); understand and use the formula in words 'length × breadth' for the area of a rectangle.
- **m** Recognise properties of rectangles.
- **n** Recognise perpendicular and parallel lines.

Introduction

The planning for the assessment units is based upon the NNS medium-term plans. There is an assessment unit for each end of half-term, as well as end-of-year assessments. Each unit consists of two detailed lesson plans, each assessing one of the key objectives, with an accompanying photocopiable activity sheet for each lesson. The notes include suggestions for further work where children have not met the objective. There are additional oral and mental, practical and written activities covering the range of key objectives taught that half-term, with photocopiable assessment sheets for written work. For the end-of-year assessment there is an assessment covering all the Year 5 key objectives, a mental assessment and a written assessment. The end-of-year assessments mirror the style of the national tests or QCA non-statutory tests. Letters alongside each objective (see left) appear alongside each assessment activity to help you identify which objectives are covered by each activity.

Using the assessment units

Choose the half-term assessment that matches your planning needs. From your ongoing teacher assessments, identify the children who you believe have achieved specific key objectives. Now decide upon the children who you suspect may have met the key objective/s but for whom you have no firm assessment data (a class record sheet has been provided on page 141 for this purpose). These children can form the target group for assessment; arrange for them to work with an adult during practical activities, who should use the probing questions included in the assessment notes for teachers. Ask all the children to complete the written assessments, putting the probing questions to the targeted group.

Supporting teaching assistants

Provide the teaching assistant with details of the activity (whether practical or written). Discuss the probing questions to be used and how responses will be recorded. Did the child give appropriate, correct responses to the questions? Was a specific question answered inappropriately? Where the latter occurs, some additional notes about what the child failed to understand would be helpful for planning future teaching. Discuss the outcomes of the assessment activity together and make notes about individual children.

Assessment for learning

Assessment is always for a purpose – here it is to check what individual children understand, know and can do, and where they need further teaching in order to achieve the key objectives. Use the outcomes of the assessment for forward planning for teaching and for homework provision. The *All New 100 Maths Lessons* (Scholastic) series provides detailed planning grids for each term, which can be used to identify further activities to support those who need more experiences in particular topics.

Assess and Review

Key objectives to be assessed

Assessment lesson 1: **Multiply and divide any positive whole integer up to 10,000 by 10 or 100 and understand the effect.**
Assessment lesson 2: **Use decimal notation for tenths and hundredths.**

Photocopiable pages
Hold the place value! (p87); Decimal ducks and drakes (p89); Digit cards (p90); Assessment test (p91-92).

Equipment
Number fans; 1-100 numeral cards; colouring pencils or coloured counters; blank 100-squares.

Assessment Activities

Mental maths assessment

1. Multiplication facts i

Ask times-table questions such as: *3 x 5; 6 x 4; 5 x 7; 3 x 8; How many lots of 9 make 36?* When you say 'Show me', the children hold up their number fans to show their answer.

Probing questions

- *Somebody needs to complete their 4 times-table. What advice could you offer to help?*
- *How are the 2 and 4 times-tables linked? Are there other times-tables linked in this way?*

2. Multiplying and dividing a

Ask the children to sit in a circle. Hold up a number card such as 34 and ask: *What would I have to do to make this read 340 or 3.4?* (Multiply by 10; divide by 10.) Give a two-digit card to one of the children, asking them to play 'Pass it on'. The child with the card reads out the number and hands it to their neighbour, with an instruction either to multiply or divide by 10 or 100. Explain that the number must not be allowed to get bigger than 10,000 nor smaller than two decimal places. Change the number cards and repeat.

Probing questions

- *What happens to the digits of a number when you multiply or divide by 10 or by 100?*
- *What is the effect of a zero in front of a set of numbers?*

Practical maths assessment

1. Ordering numbers b

Write five digits on the board and ask the children to say the biggest or the smallest number they can make with these digits. Write the answers on the board. Ask if anyone can make any numbers that fall between these two.

Probing questions

- *How can you guarantee that you have made the largest number possible from five digits? How should they be arranged? What about for the smallest number possible?*

2. Using decimal notation d

Ask the children what decimal number might fall between two whole numbers. Check their understanding of the place value.

Probing questions

- *What can you tell me about the digit 7 in these numbers: 4.7, 7.4, 74.2, 0.37?*
- *If I wanted to change 4.3 into 4.9 in one step, what would I have to do?*

Written maths assessment

Hand out copies of the written assessment to each child. Read through the first question and ask the children to complete the answer.

Probing questions

1. Short multiplication j

- *Do you need a written method to solve 7 x 7? Why? How can this help you solve 14 x 7?*
- *Estimate. How did you arrive at your estimate? How will this help you to judge the accuracy of the place value of your answer?*

2. Use all four operations k

- *What words can you look for to help you decide which operation to use for a problem?*

3. Equivalent fractions c

- *What is another way of expressing* $^6/_5$ *or* $^8/_3$*?*
- *How else could I write 50% of a number?*

Hold the place value!

Key objective:
Multiply and divide any positive whole integer up to 10,000 by 10 or 100 and understand the effect.

What you need
- A copy of 'Hold the place value!' activity sheet for each child.

Further support
Work with less confident children to support their understanding of digits, moving up and down the place value. Use digit cards on a HTU board to emphasise this, holding the empty place value with an additional 0.

Oral and mental starter

Write the following sets of numbers on the board: 3, 6, 18, 22; 4, 14, 40, 41; 30,180, 220, 60; 410, 140, 400, 40. Ask volunteers to come out and link a number with its multiple of 10. Ask them to explain how they know which multiple to choose. Discuss how, when multiplying by 10, a digit moves one place to the left and the place value is held by a 0.

Main assessment activity

Ask the children to define other rules for multiplying by 100 and dividing by 10 and 100. Talk about how digits move to the right when dividing and to the left when multiplying. This includes when the digits cross the decimal point.
Ask the children to explain why 'adding a zero' is not a good way of explaining multiplying by 10 or 100, since it does not account for decimal numbers.
Write ______ × 10 = 240 on the board, then ask: *What could the missing number be?* Then write up the following and ask the same question for each calculation: ______ × 10 = 157; 1.45 × ______ = 145; 2.9 × 100 = ______ .
Ask the children to discuss with a partner how they could solve the missing number problem. Remind them that the inverse of multiplying is dividing.

Give each child a copy of the 'Hold the place value' activity sheet to complete on their own. During the assessment activity, ask groups probing questions such as:

- *How do you know what number of places to move the digits?*
- *If you weren't sure which way to move the digits, what might help you?*
- *Do you expect the answer to a division question to get bigger or smaller?*
- *How could estimating help you?*

Plenary

Share the answers on the activity sheet. Invite individuals to explain how they worked out the answers. By the end of the lesson, the children should be able to confidently multiply and divide by 10 and 100 without actually calculating. Less confident children will still need to physically move the digit cards to change the place value.

Name Date

Hold the place value!

- Work out the missing numbers in these number sentences.

1. $65 \times \square = 6500$

2. $\square \times 10 = 840$

3. $2.1 \times 10 = \square$

4. $3.9 \times \square = 390$

5. $\square \times 100 = 720$

6. $0.34 \times 10 = \square$

7. $2.6 \times 100 = \square$

8. $\square \times 100 = 50$

9. $450 \div \square = 4.5$

10. $\square \div 10 = 3.6$

11. $176 \div 10 = \square$

12. $34.5 \div 10 = \square$

13. $43.9 \div \square = 4.39$

14. $\square \div 100 = 37.4$

15. $\square \times \square = 126$

16. $458 \div \square = \square$

Decimal ducks and drakes

Key objective:
Use decimal notation for tenths and hundredths.

What you need
- A copy of the 'Decimal Ducks and Drakes' activity sheet for each pair; either colouring pencils or coloured counters; blank 100-squares for less able children.

Further support
Less confident children may not be able to make the link between fractions and their decimal equivalent notation. A blank 100-square might be useful for them to understand that 19 hundredths is the same as saying one tenth and nine hundredths. The link between decimals and money is also helpful. Children who still cannot understand that fractions have decimal equivalents could use calculators to divide the numerator of a fraction by its denominator to create the decimal.

Oral and mental starter
Write 385.92 on the board. Point to the 8 digit and ask: *What does this digit represent?* Repeat with the 9. Ask: *What is meant by nine tenths?* Repeat the questions with the two hundredths. Ask: *How many more would I have to add to make the next whole number?* Repeat the starter with other numbers with two decimal places.

Main assessment activity
Remind the children that decimals have fraction equivalents. When we talk about nine-tenths it is actually a fraction of one whole. Ask: *What can you tell me about $^{20}/_{100}$? What is another way of saying this? How many more hundredths would I need to make one whole? Are there any other fraction equivalents that we know which can be converted to tenths?* (for example, $½ = {}^{5}/_{10} = 0.5$). Remind the children that if they put a fraction into a calculator it will give them the decimal equivalent, for example, ½ is the same as $1 \div 2 = 0.5$.

Distribute the 'Decimal ducks and drakes' activity sheet, one between each pair of children. Explain that they need to cut out the fraction cards around the edge of the sheet, shuffle them and place them face down on the table. They then need to decide whether they are going to be the 'duck' or the 'drake'. Players take it in turn to select a fraction card and to decide if it matches any of the decimals on their sheet. If it does, they must explain to their partner their reasoning and either colour the lily pad or cover it with a counter. The first person to get across the pond by covering all their decimals is the winner.

Plenary
By the end of this session, most children should be able to recognise decimal equivalents for tenths and hundredths, and some may also be able to tell you some other fractions linked to tenths. Call out some random fractions and ask the children to tell you the decimal equivalent, and vice versa.

Name Date

Decimal ducks and drakes

$\frac{20}{100}$ $\frac{3}{10}$ $\frac{1}{2}$ $\frac{60}{100}$ $\frac{54}{100}$ $\frac{21}{100}$

$1\frac{6}{10}$

$\frac{1}{5}$

$1\frac{1}{10}$

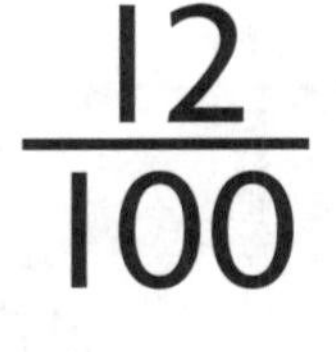

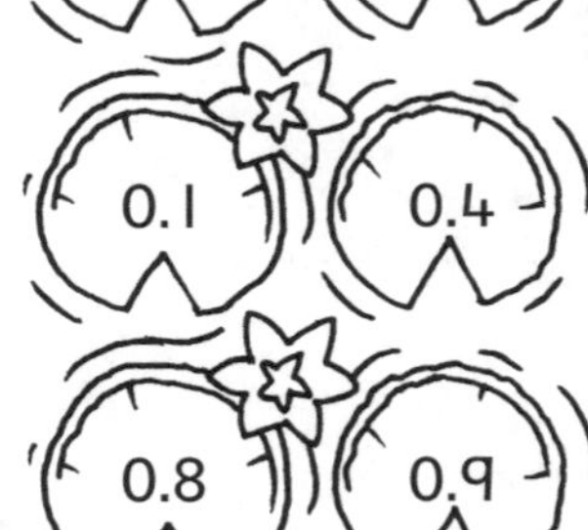

$\frac{7}{10}$

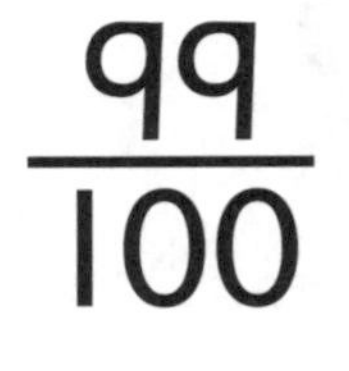

$\frac{10}{100}$

$\frac{11}{100}$ $\frac{39}{100}$ $\frac{58}{100}$ $\frac{9}{10}$ $\frac{80}{100}$ $\frac{4}{10}$

Name Date

Digit cards

0	1	2
3	4	5
6	7	8
9	0	0

H	T	U	.	t	h

Name Date

Assessment 1

1. Look at the graph below showing the number of children in a class who brought packed lunch in a week. Add the missing axis labels and a title. Add the following information: 15 children brought packed lunch on Thursday and 3 less than that on Friday. Then answer the questions at the foot of this page.

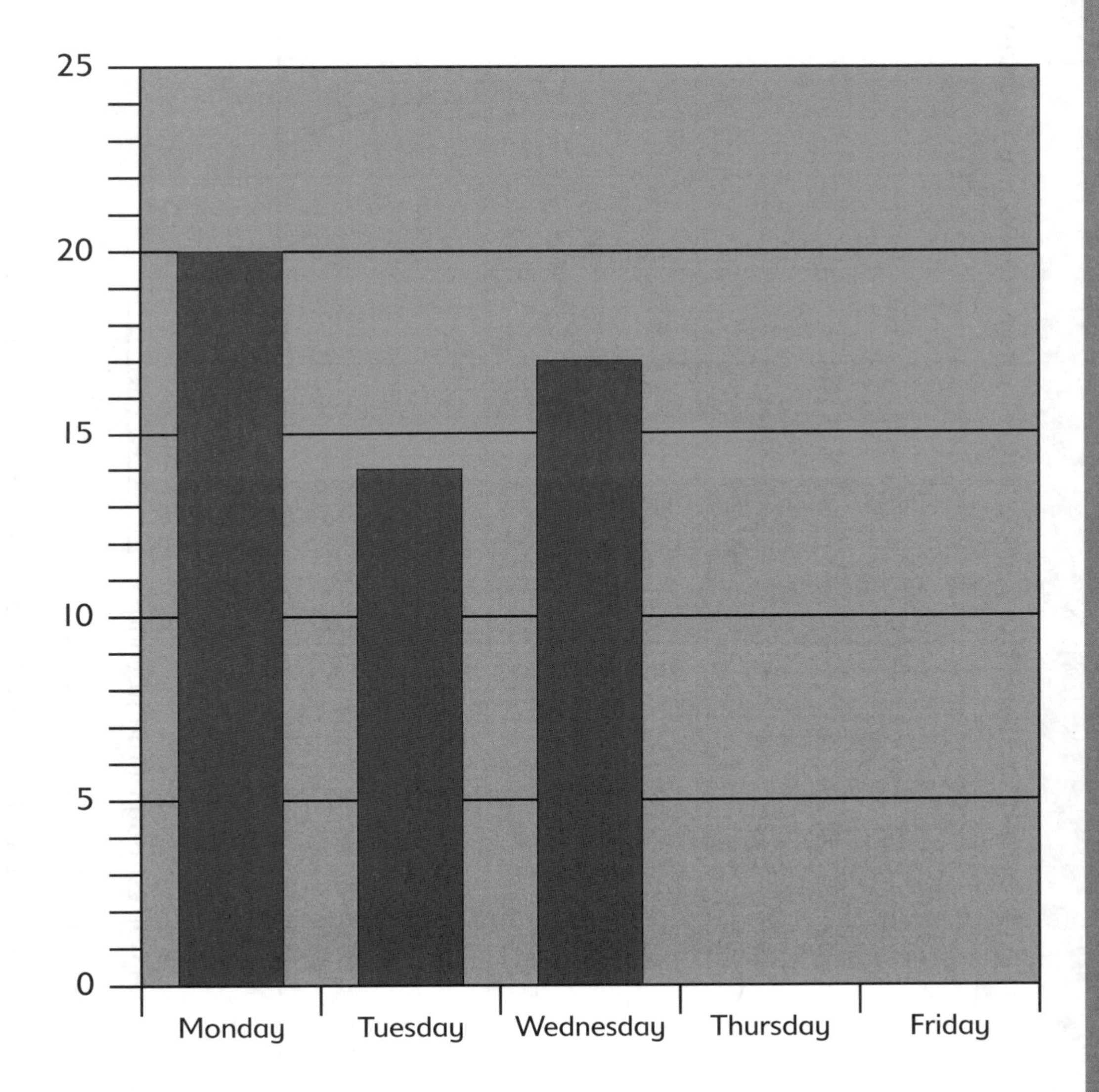

a) Which day shows the mode? ______________________

b) What was the difference between the most and least number of packed lunches? ______________________

Name Date

2. Look at the line graph below and answer the questions.

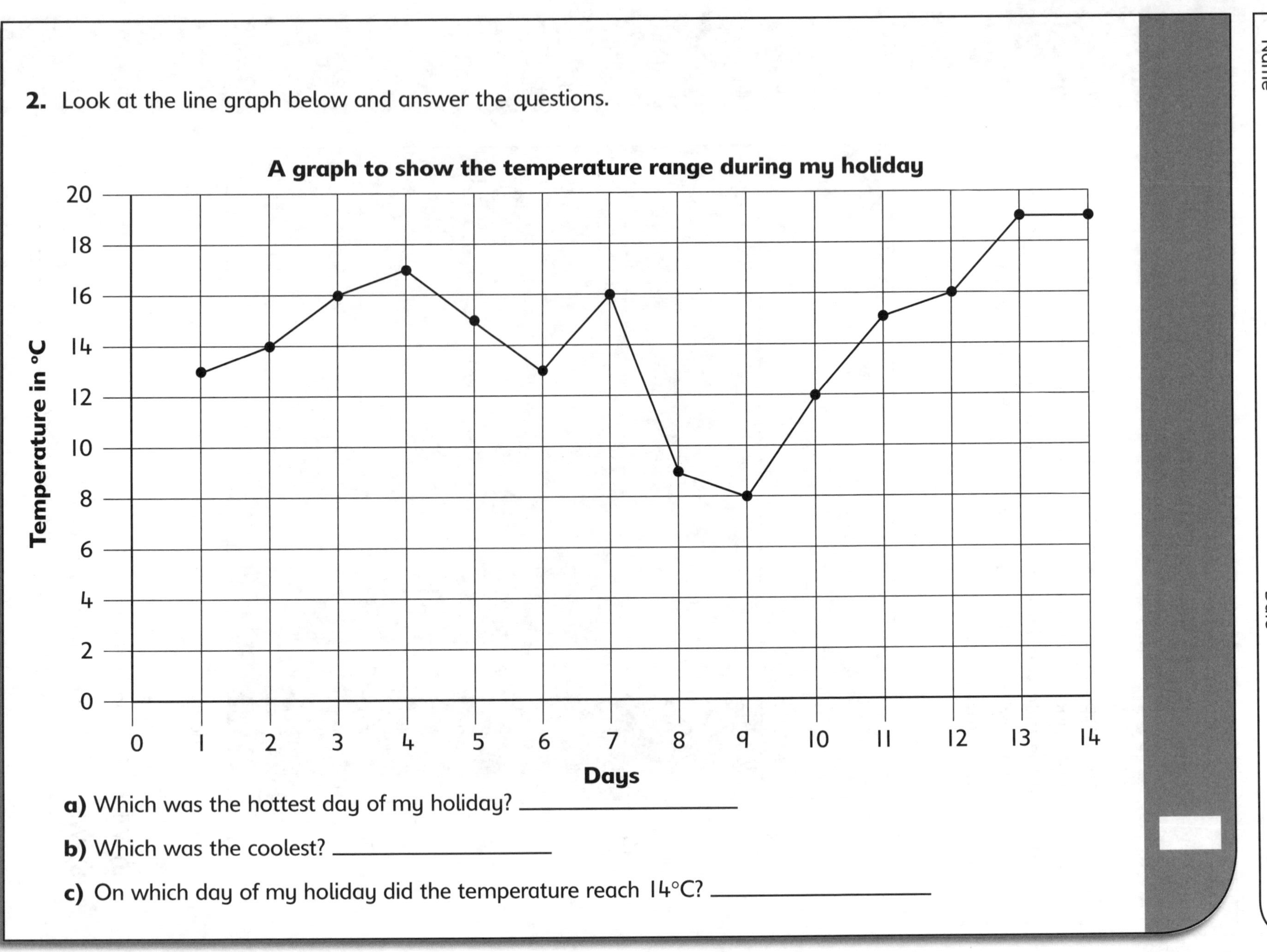

a) Which was the hottest day of my holiday? ________________

b) Which was the coolest? ________________

c) On which day of my holiday did the temperature reach 14°C? ________________

Assess and Review

Key objectives to be assessed

Assessment lesson 1: **Recognise parallel and perpendicular lines and properties of rectangles.**
Assessment lesson 2: **Calculate mentally a difference such as 8006 - 2993.**

Photocopiable pages
When is a rectangle not a rectangle? (p95); Count on me! (p97); 100-square (p98); Assessment test (p99-100).

Equipment
Number fans; individual whiteboards or paper and pens; selection of regular and irregular 2-D shapes; A4 cards with the headings Th H T U . t h.

Assessment Activities

Mental maths assessment

Multiply and divide any positive integer up to 10,000 by 10 or 100 and understand the effect a

Start with some quick-fire times-table questions to be answered using the number fans when you say 'Show me'. Next, explain that you want the children to suggest ways in which they could make 370 using multiples of 10 only (for example, 3700 ÷ 10). Children write their suggestions on their whiteboards or paper and show you.

Use digit cards to make the number 370 and write above it the headings Th H T U . t h. Ask an individual to come and explain what happens when we have 3700 divided by 10. They should say something like, *The digits stay the same and move one place to the right. The zero moves to the other side of the decimal point and it is not needed any more.* Repeat, using the children's suggestions.

Probing questions

- *If someone is struggling with their 4 times-table, what could you suggest to help them?*
- *What other links between times-tables do we know which might help us?*
- *Can you tell me what happens to a number when we multiply or divide by 10 or 100?*
- *When we multiply and the digits move to the left, what holds the place value for us?*
- *I have 38 on my calculator display. What do I have to key in to make it read 3800?*

Practical maths assessment

Multiplying by 10 or 100 a

Each child will need a set of 0-9 digit cards and a board with the headings Th H T U . t h. Ask the children to make the number 45 using the digit cards and the place value board. Now ask them to multiply that number by 10. Ask an individual to explain what they are doing. Repeat with dividing a number by 10 and again with multiplying and dividing by 100.

Probing questions

- *Can you explain why we have to put a zero in the units column when we multiplied 45 by 10? What job does that zero do?*
- *Why do 6 x 100 and 60 x 10 give the same answer?*
- *What happens when we divide 560 by 10? Where does the zero go?*

Written maths assessment

Hand out copies of the written assessment to each child. Read the first question together and give the children time to complete it.

Probing questions

1. Properties of rectangles m

- *Give me some instructions on how to draw a rectangle.*

2. Solving word problems k

- *How do you know whether to add or subtract? What clues are you looking for?*

3. Column addition and subtraction h

- *What helpful hints would you give someone to help them with column addition/subtraction?*

When is a rectangle not a rectangle?

Key objective:
Recognise parallel and perpendicular lines and properties of rectangles.

What you need
- Selection of regular and irregular 2-D shapes; 'When is a rectangle not a rectangle?' activity sheet for each child.

Further support
Some children may find reasoning about shapes difficult, particularly if they are unclear about the vocabulary of shape such as 'diagonal', 'bisect', or 'right angle.' Organise less confident children into a small group so that they can work together. Ask an adult to support the group and remind them about the meaning of the vocabulary.

Oral and mental starter
Explain that you have a number of 2-D shapes hidden in a box. Select one, still keeping it hidden, and describe its properties one by one. Ask the children to put up their hands when they think they know what shape it is. Repeat with other shapes.

Main assessment activity
Show the class a selection of 2-D shapes. Ask them to name them and describe some of the properties. Ask them to sort them into regular and irregular shapes and then into quadrilaterals and non-quadrilaterals. Finally, ask the children to tell you some rules for describing a rectangle and to sort the shapes by these criteria.

Distribute the 'When is a rectangle not a rectangle' activity sheet to individual children. Explain that it contains various 2-D shapes which they must match against the properties of a rectangle, explaining which shapes are rectangles and which are not - giving reasons where the shape does not match the properties of a rectangle.

Plenary
Most children should be clear about the properties of a rectangle. A rectangle should have: two pairs of parallel sides with each parallel pair the same length but different to each other; four right angles; diagonals that bisect in the middle; two lines of symmetry. Discuss the shapes on the activity sheet. Ask the children to explain their reasons why some of them do not fit the criteria for a rectangle.

Name Date

When is a rectangle not a rectangle?

- Think about each of these shapes in turn.
- Compare them with the description of the properties of a rectangle.
- Which of these is NOT a rectangle?
- Give reasons for your decision.

1. This is ____________________ because ____________________	**2.** This is ____________________ because ____________________
3. This is ____________________ because ____________________	**4.** This is ____________________ because ____________________
5. This is ____________________ because ____________________	**6.** This is ____________________ because ____________________
7. This is ____________________ because ____________________	**8.** This is ____________________ because ____________________

Count on me!

Key objective:
Calculate mentally a difference such as 8006 - 2993.

What you need
- A copy of the 'Count on me!' activity sheet for each child; individual whiteboards and pens.

Further support
Some children may not be able to understand the 'jump' required to round up each digit in the number and may have difficulties crossing the ten, hundreds and thousands thresholds. These children may find it helpful to use the 100-square (see p98) to round up to the next 10 then 100 and to count on with the support of a number line. An adult could then observe and record the strategy used for counting on.

Oral and mental starter

Ask a series of quick-fire difference questions around the room, starting with number bonds to 10 and 20 and then progressing to number bonds to make 100 and 1000. For example, ask: *How many more do I need to make 100 if I start with 16? What is the difference between 100 and 78? Count from 899 to make 1000.* Repeat with different numbers.

Main assessment activity

Remind the class that some seemingly large number subtractions are actually quite close and might not require a written calculation, for example 2001 - 1998. Ask the children to solve this calculation and explain how they did it. Most will say that they counted on from 1998 until they reached 2001. Now ask them to look at the following: 7002 - 1998. Ask if this calculation is any more difficult than the last one. Ask them to solve it, using their whiteboards if necessary. Remind them that they can visualise (or actually draw) a number line and count on in 'jumps' to round up each digit, starting with the units. Ask someone to demonstrate how they did this, for example:

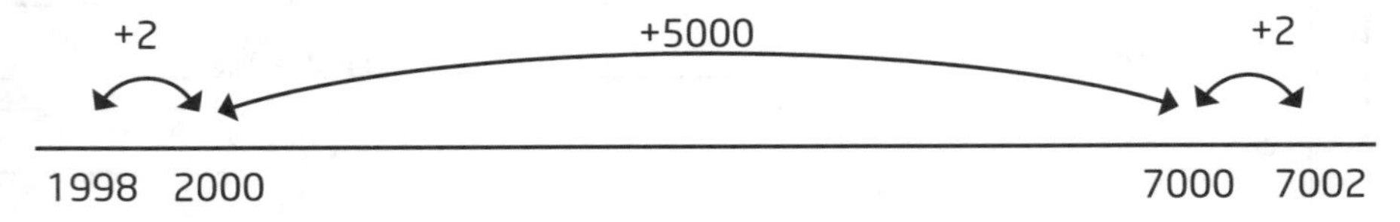

Answer 5004

Give another example, such as 6009 - 2891. Ask the children to try to calculate the answer mentally first and then explain to a partner what they did, using their whiteboards to demonstrate the 'jumps' or rounding.

Distribute the 'Count on me!' activity sheets to each child. Explain that you want them to try to calculate the differences mentally. However, if they find any of the calculations too difficult, then they may use a number line to support their counting on.

Plenary

Most children will be able to calculate the differences mentally. Knowing which children needed to use a number line will further inform your assessment. Ask the children to share their answers and talk through the steps they took.

Name Date

Count on me!

- Calculate the following sums in your head if you can.
- If there is a really tricky calculation, you may use a number line to help you.

1. 8003 – 6001 =	**2.** 7001 – 2998 =
3. 9004 – 6978 =	**4.** 6005 – 1889 =
5. 6009 – 1834 =	**6.** 7019 – 2977 =
7. 5019 – 4298 =	**8.** 5002 – 2967 =
9. 2999 – 1992 =	**10.** 7020 – 3892 =

Name Date

100-square

1	2	3	4	5	6	7	8	9	10
11	12	13	14	15	16	17	18	19	20
21	22	23	24	25	26	27	28	29	30
31	32	33	34	35	36	37	38	39	40
41	42	43	44	45	46	47	48	49	50
51	52	53	54	55	56	57	58	59	60
61	62	63	64	65	66	67	68	69	70
71	72	73	74	75	76	77	78	79	80
81	82	83	84	85	86	87	88	89	90
91	92	93	94	95	96	97	98	99	100

Name Date

Assessment 2

1. Look at this diagram of a rectangle. Draw in the diagonals.

Write some instructions to tell somebody how to draw a rectangle.

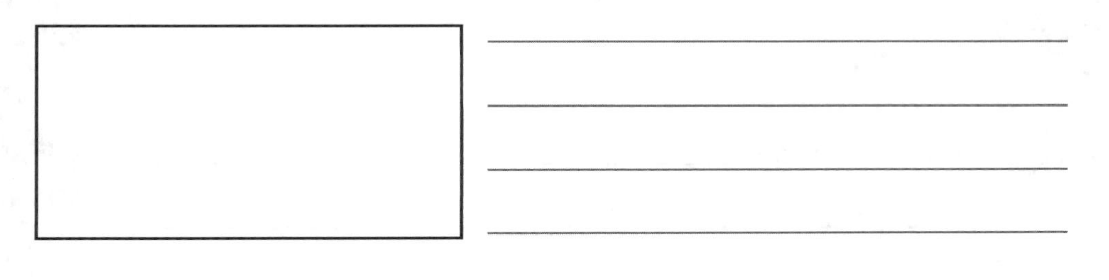

2. Solve the following problems using a vertical written method. Show all your workings.

a) 1647 – 536

b) 2543 – 1278

c) 2483 – 996

Name Date

3. Which of these calculations is incorrect? Can you correct them? What is the person doing wrong?

a)

Th	H	T	U
3	4	6	2
– 2	3	7	4
1	1	1	2

The mistake they are making is ______________________________

____

b)

Th	H	T	U
3	5	2	1
– 1	2	4	6
4	7	6	7

The mistake they are making is ______________________________

____

4. Solve these word problems in whatever way you think appropriate. Show all your thinking.

a) 2859 people attended a local football match on Saturday and 1825 attended a hockey match at the same ground on Sunday. How many people passed through the turnstiles altogether that weekend?

b) How many fewer people watched the hockey than the football?

c) Felicity had saved £138.55 towards a new computer. She needs £875.00. How much more does she need to save?

Assess and Review

Key objectives to be assessed

Assessment lesson 1: **Extend written methods to short division of HTU by U.**
Assessment lesson 2: **Relate fractions to division.**

Photocopiable pages
The great divide (p103); Divide it up and share it out! (p105); Multiplication square (p106); Assessment test (p107-108).

Equipment
1-100 number cards; 0-9 digit cards; blank cards; a decimal point card; 10-sided dice (one per pair); crayons; individual whiteboards and pens.

Assessment Activities

Mental maths assessment

1. Multiplying by 10 or 100 a

Hold up a number card and ask the children to either multiply or divide it by 10 or 100. Include decimal numbers as both questions and answers.

Probing questions

- *Why do 7 x 100 and 70 x10 give the same answer? What about 40 ÷ 10 and 400 ÷ 100?*
- *Explain a quick way of multiplying a number by 10 or by 100.*
- *Can you tell me a quick way of dividing by 10 or 100?*

2. Round a number to the nearest whole integer e

Use digit cards and a decimal point card to create both one- and two-place decimal numbers. Ask the children to round them to the nearest whole integer.

Probing questions

- *I rounded a number to the nearest integer and the answer was 41. What number could I have started with?*
- *Are there any other numbers that it could have been? What is the largest/smallest number that I could have started with? How do you know?*

Practical maths assessment

Ordering a set of integers b

Give the children a set of cards showing whole integers, such as -3, 2, 3, 0, 1. Ask them to order them from smallest to largest. Next, give the children a set of cards showing decimal integers, such as 0.3, 1.4, 1.5, 0.9, 1.0. Ask them to order them in ascending order, giving reasons for their choice. Finally, give the children a set of cards showing two-decimal place numbers, such as 4.26, 3.95, 4.12, 4.16, 4.52 and ask them to order these as before.

Probing questions

- *What do you look for first when ordering a set of numbers? Which part of each number do you look at to help you?*
- *Tell me a number that goes between these two integers: 2 and 3; 100 and 200... Which of the two integers is it closer to?*
- *Tell me two temperatures between 0°C and -10°C. Which is warmer? How can you tell?*

Written maths assessment

Hand out copies of the written assessment sheets for each child to complete.

Probing questions

1. Short division of HTU by U j

- *Talk me through your method. How do you know it is correct? What are you actually doing? What is your estimate for the 'size' of the answer?*

2. Solving word problems k

- *How do you know which operation to choose to solve this problem? What clues do you look for?*
- *How did you decide which part to do first?*

3. Relate fractions to division c

- *Tell me some fractions of numbers that equal 3, 5, 10, 20. How did you work that out?*
- *How do these relate to division questions?*

4. Recognise parallel and perpendicular lines n

- *How would you check if two lines were parallel or perpendicular?*
- *Give someone instructions for measuring accurately using a protractor.*

The great divide

Key objective:
Extend written methods to short division of HTU by U.

What you need
- Copies of 'The great divide' activity sheet for each child; a set of 0-9 digit cards for each group of 4-6 children.

Further support
Some children may not have the times-tables recall required to do short division and may need the support of a multiplication square and easier divisors. An adult should work with these children to remind them of how any remainders in the division question cannot be ignored but must be 'transferred along' to the next place value for division.

Oral and mental starter

Play 'Division Bingo'. Give each group a random selection of six of their digit cards, which they place face up in the centre of their table, where everyone can see them. Say assorted division facts up to 10×10. When the group finds the answer among its cards, one of them turns it over. The winning group is the first one to turn all of its cards over correctly. Ask questions such as: *What is 36 ÷ 6; ...½ of 16; ...24 shared among four people.*

Main assessment activity

Remind the class that they were able to use their times-table knowledge to divide bigger numbers by taking each place value in turn - say, 426 divided by 3. Ask for a volunteer to demonstrate this, while you record each part of the process as follows:

Step 1 Round the number and estimate: $400 \div 3 \approx 133$.

$$3\overline{)4\,{}^{1}2\,6}$$
$$1\;4\;2$$

Step 2 $4 \div 3 = 1\text{ r }1$
Ask: *What should I do with the remainder?* (Pass it on to stand with the 2.)

Step 3 $12 \div 3 = 4$ (no remainder).

Step 4 $6 \div 3 = 2$.

Answer = 142

Ask the children to consider the following sum and spot where you have gone wrong:

$$4\overline{)5\,4\,8}$$
$$1\;1\;2$$

Estimate: $500 \div 4 \approx 122$. The remainder has not been transferred along and since its value is 100, this makes a considerable difference to the answer. It should read:

$$4\overline{)5\,{}^{1}4\,{}^{2}8}$$
$$1\;3\;7$$

Distribute copies of 'The great divide' assessment sheet to each child and explain that they should try to use the short division method to answer the questions. For extra support and accuracy, some children might like to record each step of their calculation at the side.

Plenary

Ask individuals to demonstrate how they answered the questions, talking through their methods. Most children should be secure with short division. Ask: *What is the most common error made when doing short division?*

Name Date

The great divide

- Complete the following questions using short division.
  - If it helps, record each step at the side as you go.
  - Don't forget to estimate first!

1. $3\overline{)441}$	2. $4\overline{)832}$
3. $5\overline{)715}$	4. $8\overline{)256}$
5. $6\overline{)906}$	6. $4\overline{)468}$
7. $5\overline{)851}$	8. $3\overline{)908}$
9. $7\overline{)812}$	10. $6\overline{)137}$

Divide it up and share it out!

Key objective:
Relate fractions to division.

What you need

- Copies of the 'Divide it up and share it out!' activity sheet for each child; 10-sided dice (one per pair of children); colouring crayons; individual whiteboards and pens.

Further support

Some children will find this activity tricky simply because they do not have secure times-tables knowledge. Provide them with a multiplication square to support this (see p106). Some children may experience difficulties when finding multiple fractions such as $^2/_3$ of 27. In this instance, ask them to work with an adult and record their thinking in longhand, eg $^1/_3$ of 27 = 9; $^1/_3 + ^1/_3 = ^2/_3$, so 9 + 9 = 18, which is $^2/_3$ of 27.

Oral and mental starter

Using individual whiteboards and pens, ask the children to write the number 6 in the centre of their board and give them two minutes to write as many division facts as they can to make this number. At the end of the given time, ask them to hold up their boards to show you. Repeat with 5, 12 and 8.

Main assessment activity

Ask the class to remind you what they understand by fractions. How would they find a fraction of a number such as ¼ of 40? What skills are they using to find a fraction of a number? Ask them to explain to you how they would find a multiple fraction such as ¾ of 40. Invite a volunteer to write the process on the board to remind everyone else. For example, ¼ of 40 = 10, therefore ¾ of 40 = 10 + 10 +10 = 30.

Distribute copies of the 'Divide it up and share it out!' activity sheet, along with one dice between each pair of children. Explain to the children that they are going to play a game to practise finding fractions of numbers by dividing. Each player throws the dice to generate an answer; they must then find a corresponding question on their sheet, fill in the answer and colour in the square. The winner is the person to have five coloured squares in a row, either upwards, across or diagonally, or the most coloured squares by the end of the lesson. Ensure that the children are clear about the rules of the game before beginning.

Plenary

Most children should be able to calculate fractions of numbers mentally. A few children may seek the reassurance of jotting down multiple fractions to ensure accurate adding.

Name Date

Divide it up and share it out!

$\frac{1}{2}$ of 12 =	$\frac{1}{10}$ of 50 =	$\frac{2}{7}$ of 21 =	$\frac{2}{5}$ of 15 =	$\frac{3}{8}$ of 24 =
$\frac{1}{9}$ of 72 =	$\frac{2}{6}$ of 30 =	$\frac{2}{3}$ of 12 =	$\frac{1}{8}$ of 56 =	$\frac{3}{4}$ of 8 =
$\frac{1}{2}$ of 14 =	$\frac{2}{4}$ of 16 =	$\frac{2}{5}$ of 20 =	$\frac{1}{100}$ of 100 =	$\frac{1}{9}$ of 27 =
$\frac{2}{3}$ of 9 =	$\frac{3}{4}$ of 4 =	$\frac{1}{7}$ of 35 =	$\frac{2}{5}$ of 10 =	$\frac{2}{7}$ of 28 =
$\frac{2}{8}$ of 40 =	$\frac{1}{6}$ of 42 =	$\frac{3}{8}$ of 16 =	$\frac{1}{4}$ of 16 =	$\frac{3}{5}$ of 10 =

Name Date

Multiplication square

×	1	2	3	4	5	6	7	8	9	10
1	1	2	3	4	5	6	7	8	9	10
2	2	4	6	8	10	12	14	16	18	20
3	3	6	9	12	15	18	21	24	27	30
4	4	8	12	16	20	24	28	32	36	40
5	5	10	15	20	25	30	35	40	45	50
6	6	12	18	24	30	36	42	48	54	60
7	7	14	21	28	35	42	49	56	63	70
8	8	16	24	32	40	48	56	64	72	80
9	9	18	27	36	45	54	63	72	81	90
10	10	20	30	40	50	60	70	80	90	100

Name Date

Assessment 3

1. Calculate the following:

2) 264   3) 642   4) 602

2. Look at the following calculations. Decide which are correct and which are incorrect. Can you explain where the person went wrong?

a) 3) 2 3 6
1 2

b) 5) 1 0 8 5
2 0 1 7

c) 8) 3 2 8
4 2

3. Choose the correct operation to solve these problems.

a) Tariq has received equal numbers of postcards from eight different countries. He has received a total of 176 cards. How many cards came from each country?

b) Alison's cat has had eight kittens. Her mum says that she may sell them. She advertises them for £18 each. If she sells them all, how much money will she have? At the last minute she decides to keep one of the kittens. How much money does she finally make?

c) A car park attendant sets his assistant a riddle: 'There are only cars in the park today,' he says, 'and there are 944 wheels touching our tarmac. How many cars is that?' The assistant worked it out and then challenged his boss by saying, '32 motorbikes have just driven in. How many wheels are there now?'

Name Date

4. Work out the following calculations:

a) $\frac{1}{4}$ of 32

b) $\frac{3}{4}$ of 36

c) $\frac{1}{3}$ of 27

d) $\frac{2}{3}$ of 30

e) $\frac{1}{6}$ of 42

f) $\frac{5}{6}$ of 54

5. Draw and label a horizontal line and two parallel perpendicular lines.

6. Use a protractor to measure these angles.

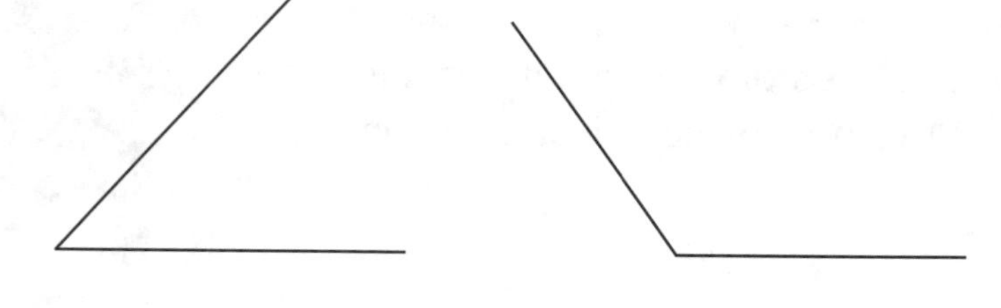

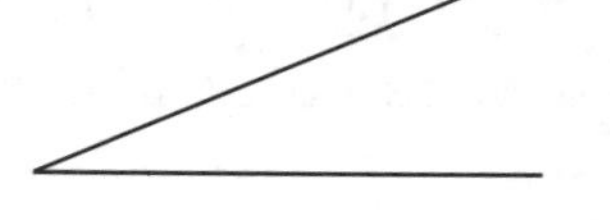

Assess and Review

Key objectives to be assessed

Assessment lesson 1: **Understand area measured in square centimetres (cm^2). Understand and use the formula in words 'length x breadth' for the area of a rectangle.**
Assessment lesson 2: **Extend written methods to column addition of two integers less than 10,000.**

Photocopiable pages
This is my area! (p111); It all adds up! (p113); Number fans (p114); Assessment test (p115-116).

Equipment
1-100 number cards; 0-9 digit cards; negative digit cards -1 to -9; individual whiteboards and pens (or pencil and paper); calculators.

Assessment Activities

Mental maths assessment

1. Relate fractions to division c

Ask questions such as: *What is $^1/_4$ of 16? ...$^1/_3$ of 12? ...$^1/_5$ of 25?* and so on.

Probing questions

- *How do we find one fraction of a number?*
- *What are we actually doing to find a fraction?*
- *How is the denominator helpful when finding fractions?*
- *If I can find $^1/_3$ of a number, how would I calculate $^2/_3$?*

2. Rounding numbers e

Write a number on the board. Ask whether it should be rounded up or down to the nearest whole integer. Children display this whole number on their number fans when you say 'Show me'.

Probing questions

- *In the number 4.27, what is the value of the 2?*
- *How many more would I have to add to 7.6 to make the next whole integer? How about 9.86?*
- *How do I decide whether a number is to be rounded up or down?*

3. Multiplication facts i

Ask the children to display the answers to quick-fire multiplication facts on their number fans and hold them up when you say 'Show me'.

Probing questions

- *If someone has forgotten their 8 times-table, can you suggest tips to help them work it out?*

Practical maths assessment

Relate fractions to their decimal representation f

Ask the children to remind you what a fraction is, and what each part of the fraction means. Remind them that a fraction can be converted to a decimal, using a calculator. Ask them to use this knowledge to find decimal equivalents for $^1/_4$, $^1/_2$, $^1/_5$, $^2/_{10}$, $^1/_{10}$, $^6/_{10}$ and $^3/_4$. Ask them to explain what each part of the decimal representation means.

Probing questions

- *Why do we get the same answer for $^1/_5$ as $^2/_{10}$?*
- *Do I need a calculator to show me the decimal equivalent of tenths? Why not?*

Written maths assessment

Hand out copies of the written assessment sheets for each child to complete.

Probing questions

1. Solving word problems k

- *If I have an answer of 3.2m, what could the question have been?*
- *How are you going to check your calculation?*

2. Column addition and subtraction h

- *Is this calculation correct? What has the person done wrong? How could you help them correct it?*
- *What could you do first to give you a feeling for the size of answer you are looking for?*
- *How could you check your calculation?*

3. Area measured in cm^2/Understand and use the formula 'length x breadth' l

- *Can you tell me a rule for working out the area of a rectangle? Will it work for all rectangles?*
- *Estimate the area of the front of your book. How did you do this? If the area of a rectangle is $24cm^2$, what are the possible lengths of the sides? Are there other possible answers? How did you work it out?*

This is my area!

Key objective:
Understand area measured in square centimetres (cm^2). Understand and use the formula in words 'length x breadth' for the area of a rectangle.

What you need
- Copies of the 'This is my area!' activity sheet; calculators; number fans (see p114).

Further support
Some children may find multiplying difficult, and may find a multiplication square or calculator helpful. For some, the concept of area is more difficult, and they may need support from an adult to understand what they are doing when multiplying 'length × breadth'.

Oral and mental starter

Distribute number fans to each child and explain that they are going to answer some quick-fire multiplication questions by finding the appropriate answer on their number fans and holding it up when you say 'Show me'. Call out questions such as: *5 × 8; six lots of 3; 4 multiplied by 9.* Each time, check accuracy by looking at the number fans.

Main assessment activity

Hold up for the whole class to see something that is rectangular in shape - for example, a book. Ask the children how they might measure the area of the book. Children should be able to remember the formula 'length × breadth'. Remind them that if they draw a rectangle on some squared paper, the area is the number of squares within that rectangle, but is more quickly calculated by measuring the length of one side and the breadth of the other and multiplying them together. Draw some rectangles on the board and label their sides. Ask the children to work out the area and show you using the answer on their number fans.

Then draw a five-sided shape or an irregular quadrilateral and ask the children if they can still use the same formula to find the area of this shape. Remind them that the formula only works for squares and rectangles, but may also be used for composite shapes, such as an 'L' shape, if they can be subdivided into rectangles.

Explain to the children that they are each going to apply the formula 'length × breadth' by looking for rectangular shapes around the room, measuring the length and breadth and finding the area. Ask them to record their measurements and the area on their assessment sheet. Calculators may be used to work out difficult multiples. Warn against climbing to reach out-of-the way rectangles such as windows.

Plenary

Check that suitable shapes have been chosen. Most children should be able to find an area accurately. Choose a few to measure and check as a class. Draw a composite shape such as an 'H' shape, label the sides and ask for volunteers to demonstrate how to find the area.

This is my area!

- Find eight rectangular-shaped items in the room.
- Use rulers or tape measures to measure them accurately.
- Record the item and the measurements in the spaces provided.
- Work out the area and express it in the correct unit of measurement.

Item: Measurements: Area:	Item: Measurements: Area:
Item: Measurements: Area:	Item: Measurements: Area:
Item: Measurements: Area:	Item: Measurements: Area:
Item: Measurements: Area:	Item: Measurements: Area:

It all adds up!

Key objective:
Extend written methods to column addition of two integers less than 10,000.

What you need
- Copies of the 'It all adds up!' activity sheet; individual whiteboards and pens.

Further support
Some children will not be able to remember to 'carry' the next place value digits and may still need to use the expanded method for column addition where they add each place value separately. An adult should sit with these children and observe and record the ways in which they solve these problems.

Oral and mental starter

Explain that the oral and mental starter is against the clock. The children are going to write down as many number bonds as they can in one minute to make a given number (for example, number bonds to 10). The children write down all the combinations that they know, adding only. Repeat with 15, 12 and 20.

Main assessment activity

Write on the board the following numbers: £2.56; £7.93; £17.49. Ask the class to decide if they think that adding these is a mental or a written calculation. Ask for volunteers to demonstrate the method they prefer to use to add these numbers. Some children may use the expanded method of column addition and others may use the standard method.

Discuss how column addition is set out with the decimal places all lined up one underneath another. Remind the children of the importance of the correct place value, whether adding the most significant digits first or whether 'carrying' to the next place value:

```
    £2.56           £2.56
 +  £7.93        +  £7.93
   £17.49          £17.49
   ------          ------
   £26.00          £27.98
    £1.80             1 1 1
    £0.18
   ------
   £27.98
```

Distribute copies of the activity sheet 'It all adds up!' and ask the children to answer the questions independently, using whichever column addition method they prefer.

Plenary

Share some of the examples together, asking volunteers to come and demonstrate and talk through their methods on the board. Write this incorrect example on the board and ask the children to spot the mistakes.

```
    £7.46
 +  £2.85
    £3.97
   £12.18
```

None of the extra 'carried' digits have been included.

Name Date

It all adds up!

- Complete the following questions using your preferred method of column addition.

1. 386 + 179	**2.** £68.37 + £78.32
3. 299 + 326	**4.** £9.56 + £7.83 £4.77
5. 782 + 563	**6.** £67.20 + £45.99
7. 291 + 355 + 182	**8.** £16.59 + £35.02
9. Michael measured the distance between classroom doors at school. They were 6.2m, 4.95m, 2.9m and 5.50m. What was the total distance he measured?	**10.** Kelly held a charity cake stall at breaktime over three days. On the first day she made £6.45, on the second day she made £5.24 and on the third day she made £7.78. How much money did Kelly collect for her charity altogether?

Name Date

Number fans

0 1 2 3 4

5 6 7 8 9

Name Date

Assessment 4

1. What would be the area of a rectangle whose sides measure 8cm and 5cm?

2. If the area of a rectangle is 32cm^2, what could the sides measure?

3. Karen says that a square with sides of 7cm has an area of 28cm. Is she right? Why?

4. What is the rule for working out the area of a rectangle?

Name Date

5. Calculate the following and show a method of checking the answer for each.

a)
```
  5 4 2
+ 3 2 9
```

b)
```
  8 6 8
+ 6 8 5
```

c)
```
  7 8 5
- 2 4 7
```

d)
```
  1 0 3 5
-   5 6 8
```

6. Are the following calculations correct? What is wrong with them? Correct them.

a)
```
  3 8 4
+ 2 2 5
  5 0 9
```

b)
```
  9 4 2
- 2 5 8
  7 1 6
```

7. Alan needed 842 bricks to extend his garden wall. He already had 102 left over from another project. How many more did he have to buy?

8. Jennie earned £30 per day and Ann earned £17 per day while serving in a teashop. They worked for six days of their holiday. How much did each girl earn over her holiday?

Assess and Review

Key objectives to be assessed

Assessment lesson 1: **Extend written methods to long multiplication of TU by TU.**
Assessment lesson 2: **Relate fractions to their decimal representation.**

Photocopiable pages
The long multiplication road (p119); Equal shares for all (p121); Equivalent fractions, decimals and percentages (p122); Assessment test (p123-124).

Equipment
Number fans; blank cards on which to write a set of integers for ordering; A4 cards with the headings Th H T U . t h.

Assessment Activities

Mental maths assessment

1. Multiply by 10 or 100 a

Ask: *What number could I have started with if I multiplied by 100 and ended up with 7800?* Repeat with other numbers multiplied and divided by 10 or 100.

Probing questions

- *Why do 6 x 100 and 60 x 10 give the same answer? What about 40 ÷ 10 and 400 ÷ 100?*
- *Explain a quick way of multiplying/dividing a number by 10 or by 100.*

2. Round a number to the nearest whole integer e

Ask the children to think of numbers that could be rounded to 6000, 600 or 60.

Probing questions

- *Can I use the same rule for rounding up or down decimals as for rounding to whole tens, hundreds or thousands?*
- *What whole integer would you round 4.49 to? What about 4.51?*

3. Know multiplication facts to 10 x 10 i

Ask the children to generate the 13 or 14 times-tables using their 10 x 10 known facts, eg 2 x 10 = 20, 2 x 3 = 6, so 2 x 13 = 26.

Probing questions

- *What other links between times-tables can be useful?*

Practical maths assessment

1. Relate fractions to decimals f

Each child will need a set of 0-9 digit cards and a board with the headings TH H T U . t h. Use the fraction and decimal equivalence cards to ask questions. Start with $^1/_{10}$ and ask the children to represent it on their place value boards using digit cards. Repeat with other fractions such as ½, ¼, ¾, $^1/_5$. Each time, ask the children to explain how they know the decimal equivalents.

Probing questions

- *Explain how $^1/_{10}$ is equivalent to 0.1.*
- *What is the fraction equivalent of 0.4? How do you know? Is this the simplest form of the fraction?*

2. Order a set of integers b

Give the children a set of cards showing whole integers, such as 6.8, 6.5, 7.1, 5.8. Ask them to order the cards from smallest to largest, explaining their choice.

Probing questions

- *If the midpoint of two whole numbers is 8.5, what could the numbers be?*
- *6.85 is the midpoint between 6.8 and which other number?*

Written maths assessment

Hand out copies of the written assessment sheets for each child to complete.

Probing questions

- *Look at this calculation. Is it correct? Can you estimate the likely answer?*
- *In a calculation such as 37 x 14, what two numbers are multiplied together to make 370?*
- *What are the clues you look for when solving a multiplication word problem?*
- *How much does 100% represent?*
- *How can your knowledge of decimal equivalents help you to find some percentages?*
- *Can you tell me the difference between ratio and proportion?*

The long multiplication road

Key objective:
Extend written methods to long multiplication of TU by TU.

What you need
- Copies of 'The long multiplication road' activity sheet for each child; number fans (see p114).

Further support
Some children may find it difficult to progress to multiplication of TU x TU and will need the support of an adult. They could also use a multiplication grid to support their times-tables and the grid method rather than long multiplication.

Oral and mental starter

Distribute number fans to each child. Explain that they are going to find the answers to some multiplication questions and show the answers on their number fans. The questions are going to be on times-tables but using multiples of 10, for example 3 × 20; 50 multiplied by 7; 30 lots of 9.

Main assessment activity

Remind the class about the methods they have been using to multiply bigger numbers, either HTU × U or TU × TU. Depending on your school calculation policy, some children may still be using the grid method; however, many children should be able to multiply vertically. Write the following calculation on the board and ask children who have differing strategies to come and demonstrate how they would solve it.

34 × 16 =

```
   3 4
 × 1 6    Start by multiplying by 6 units
 2 0 4    Don't forget to 'carry' across the 20 from 24 and
  (2)     add it with the 10 multiplication (3×6) = 18+2 = 20.
 3 4 0    Put in a place-holder zero in order to multiply by
 5 4 4    a multiple of 10. Finally, add together.
```

Discuss common problems and difficulties that might arise with long multiplication.

Distribute copies of 'The long multiplication road' activity sheet to each child. Ask them to use their preferred long multiplication method to answer the questions.

Plenary

Write up a question such as 45 × 14. Ask for a volunteer to calculate this using long multiplication while you complete the same calculation using the grid method. Ask: *Which two numbers multiplied together give the answer 400?* (40 × 10.) Discuss how the grid method allows you to see each whole-number answer, whereas the long multiplication method relies on accurate place value recording and 'carrying' digits into the next place value.

Name Date

The long multiplication road

- Answer the following questions using your preferred written multiplication method.

1. 36×14	**2.** 18×27
3. 45×21	**4.** 51×24
5. 35×23	**6.** 54×32
7. 73×25	**8.** 63×28
9. Cara collected 15 sets of animal stickers. There were 25 stickers in each set. How many individual stickers has she got?	**10.** There were 28 rows of 41 chairs in a theatre. How many seats were there altogether?

Equal shares for all

Key objective:
Relate fractions to their decimal representation.

What you need

- A copy of the 'Equal shares for all' activity sheet for each child; an A3 copy of the 'Equivalent fractions, decimals and percentages' sheet (p122), plus another copy of this sheet to cut out and make cards; number fans.

Further support

Some children may still find the concept of equivalence difficult. Decimal equivalents can be demonstrated by using a calculator and entering the fraction, eg $\frac{3}{4} = 3 \div 4 = 0.75$. An adult should work with this group and they should have access to the equivalence general resource sheet to help match equivalents. The adult should listen to the child's reasoning and record their understanding.

Oral and mental starter

Using number fans, the children should be able to find simple fractions of numbers and reveal them to you when you say 'Show me'. Ask questions such as: $\frac{1}{2}$ of 30; $\frac{1}{4}$ of 24; $\frac{2}{3}$ of 6.

Main assessment activity

Display the enlarged copy of the 'Equivalent fractions, decimals and percentages' sheet (p122). Ask the children to make generalisations about the pattern that they see. Ask them to explain how $\frac{1}{4}$, $\frac{1}{2}$ and $\frac{3}{4}$ can be converted – for example, $\frac{1}{4} = \frac{25}{100} = 0.25$. Remind them that as long as a fraction can be multiplied up to make tenths or hundredths, the decimal equivalent can easily be found.

Explain to the children that they will be working individually to make a 'domino trail' where the two touching edges of the domino must have a matching value, fraction and decimal. They must work out the equivalent and fill it in on the 'Equal shares for all' activity sheet. The dominoes may then be cut out and the game played with a partner.

Plenary

Cut up the general resource 'Equivalent fractions, decimals and percentages' into cards and share them out around the room. Ask individual children to hold up their card and read its value out loud. The children holding the matching equivalent cards must quickly stand up, holding up their cards. The first person standing wins the 'set' for their table. Continue until all the sets have been collected. The children should be able to demonstrate some speed and confidence at recognising the equivalent values.

Name Date

Equal shares for all

- Complete the domino snake by ensuring that the dominoes have an equivalent fraction and decimal at adjoining ends.
- Cut out the dominoes carefully, shuffle them and take six each.
- The person who has 1.0 starts. Take it in turns to match the dominoes to either end. If you do not have a matching domino that you can place in the chain, miss a turn. The winner is the first to have laid down all their dominoes.

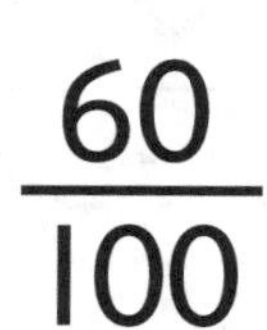

Domino 1		Domino 2	
$\frac{60}{100}$	$\frac{10}{10}$	$\frac{3}{4}$	0.3
$\frac{1}{5}$	0.75	1.0	$\frac{1}{4}$
0.1	$\frac{8}{10}$	$\frac{9}{10}$	0.7
$\frac{7}{10}$	0.6	$\frac{80}{100}$	0.2
0.25	$\frac{4}{10}$	$\frac{1}{2}$	0.9
$\frac{30}{100}$	0.5	0.4	$\frac{1}{10}$

Name Date

Equivalent fractions, decimals and percentages

$\frac{1}{10}$ or $\frac{10}{100}$	0.1	10%
$\frac{2}{10}$ or $\frac{20}{100}$	0.2	20%
$\frac{1}{4}$ or $\frac{25}{100}$	0.25	25%
$\frac{3}{10}$ or $\frac{30}{100}$	0.3	30%
$\frac{4}{10}$ or $\frac{40}{100}$	0.4	40%
$\frac{5}{10}$ or $\frac{50}{100}$ or $\frac{1}{2}$	0.5	50%
$\frac{6}{10}$ or $\frac{60}{100}$	0.6	60%
$\frac{7}{10}$ or $\frac{70}{100}$	0.7	70%
$\frac{3}{4}$ or $\frac{75}{100}$	0.75	75%
$\frac{8}{10}$ or $\frac{80}{100}$	0.8	80%
$\frac{9}{10}$ or $\frac{90}{100}$	0.9	90%
$\frac{10}{10}$ or $\frac{100}{100}$ or 1	1.0	100%

Name Date

Assessment 5

1. Complete the following calculations and use different methods to check your answers.

 a) 45 × 17 =

 b) 38 × 16 =

2. Are the following calculations correct? If not, explain where a mistake has been made and correct it.

H	T	U
	5	3
x	1	5
	1	5
	2	5
		3
		5
	4	8

H	T	U
	6	4
x	2	3
1	9	2
1	2	8
3	2	0

3. Calculate the following using either the grid method or standard long multiplication:

 37 × 14

WEEK 7 Half-term assessment

Name Date

4. a) The school secretary orders pencils in boxes of 12. She orders 32 boxes. How many pencils is that altogether?

b) If each pencil costs 8p, how much money was spent?

5. Find:

a) 25% of 36 **b)** 50% of 82 **c)** 10% of 90

d) 20% of 30 **e)** 12% of 50 **f)** 15% of 30

6. In our classroom there is a ratio of chairs to tables of 4:1. We have 32 chairs. How many tables do we have?

7. a) In a bag of toffees and creams, the proportion of toffees is 3/5. What is the ratio?

b) If there are 45 sweets in a bag, how many of them will be toffees?

Assess and Review

Key objectives to be assessed

Assessment lesson 1: **Extend written methods to column subtraction of more than two integers less than 10,000.**

Assessment lesson 2: **Use all four operations to solve simple word problems involving numbers and quantities based on 'real life', money and measures (including time).**

Photocopiable pages

You can't take the top from the bottom! (p127); Operation calculate (p129); Clue words (p130); Assessment test (p131-132).

Equipment

Individual whiteboards and pens (or pencils and paper for informal jottings); number fans.

Assessment Activities

Mental maths assessment

1. Relate fractions to decimals f

Ask the children to convert fraction numbers to decimal equivalents, for example 2½ = 2.5.

Probing questions

- *How do I know that $5^1/_{10}$ is the same as 5.1?*
- *What is the fraction equivalent of 5.2? How else could I express this fraction?*
- *Can you tell me the decimal equivalent of $5^4/_5$?*

2. Order a given set of positive and negative integers b

Ask the children to choose the coldest of a list of temperatures, including both positive and negative numbers, eg -3, -1, 0, 3, 5, 6°C.

Probing questions

- *Can you explain why you chose this as the coldest?*
- *What temperature would be one/ten degrees colder than -3°C?*

3. Know by heart all multiplication facts up to 10 x 10 i

Ask the children the answers to quick-fire times-tables questions, using their number fans and showing you their answers when you say 'Show me'.

Probing questions

- *How can inverting multiplication facts help us to solve tricky times-tables?*
- *What is meant by 'instant recall'?*

Practical maths assessment

Use all four operations k

Ask the children to demonstrate, using informal jottings, how they would solve problems such as: *A shop has reduced all sports wear by 20%. What would the new price of a £50 pair of trainers be?* Repeat with 15% or 12%, or fractions such as ¾ of 32. Look for step-by-step calculating.

Probing questions

- *How would you calculate 20% or 12% or 15%? Is there an equivalent? What fact do you know that you can find? Show me how.*

Written maths assessment

Hand out copies of the written assessment sheets for each child to complete.

Probing questions

- *Look at this calculation. Is it correct? Can you estimate the likely answer? What should be corrected?*
- *In a calculation such as 37 x 10, how does your knowledge of place value help you find an answer?*
- *Would you expect the answer to a division sum to be bigger or smaller? What implications does this have for the place value?*
- *What are the clues you look for when solving a subtraction/addition word problem?*
- *What have you got to be careful about when doing column addition/subtraction?*

You can't take the top from the bottom!

Key objective:
Extend written methods to column subtraction of more than two integers less than 10,000.

What you need
- Copies of the 'You can't take the top from the bottom!' activity sheet for each child; number fans (see p114).

Further support
Some children will find decomposition in the traditional compact column subtraction very difficult to comprehend. They will need support to set out the expanded method in order to see clearly what they are doing. This group will need to work with an adult who can track their strategies and guide where necessary.

Oral and mental starter

The children will use number fans to answer some subtraction or difference questions, displaying the answer when you say 'Show me'. Ask questions such as: *What is the difference between 58 and 76? How many more do I need to add to 856 to make 1000? What is 73 take away 19?*

Main assessment activity

Write an example of a subtraction question on the board for the whole class, for example: 1327 - 583. Discuss whether this difference is a manageable counting-on problem or if it would be more accurate to do a written calculation. Work through this as column subtraction together on the board. Demonstrate both the compact and expanded methods in order to highlight the problem of taking the eight (or 80) away from the two (20).

```
  2 1
 1̶3̶2̶7          1327  ────►   1̶0̶0̶0̶ + 3̶0̶0̶ + 2̶0̶ + 7   (1200 + 120)
-  583        -  583  ────►          500 + 80 + 3
   744           744                 700 + 40 + 4
```

Discuss what is happening when a number is partitioned and reorganised; liken it to the decomposition of the standard method.

Distribute copies of the 'You can't take the top from the bottom!' activity sheet to each child. Discuss the title of the worksheet and the clue that it provides in order to avoid one of the common mistakes made when doing subtraction. Ask the children to work on the sheet to answer the questions independently.

Plenary

Ask for volunteers to demonstrate their chosen methods for solving subtraction problems. Most children should have a written strategy that they are comfortable using, and should be able to explain it to each other. Ask the children to look at question 6 together and describe to a partner how they dealt with the mixed units of pounds and pence. Discuss how it makes a difference with the expanded method, but makes no difference at all for the compact method.

You can't take the top from the bottom!

- Use your preferred subtraction method to solve these questions.

1. 1487 – 623	**2.** 4824 – 1263
3. 2081 – 973	**4.** 3103 – 1297
5. 4185 – 1297	**6.** £315.27 – £82.53
7. £120.38 – £73.59	**8.** £ 835.22 – £768.24
9. Sami had £102.69 in his bank account. He spent £39.49 on a computer game. How much has he got left?	**10.** Out of 1036 children in a secondary school, 827 of them wear black school shoes. How many do not?

Operation calculate

Key objective:
Use all four operations to solve simple word problems involving numbers and quantities based on 'real life', money and measures (including time).

What you need
- A copy of the 'Operation calculate!' activity sheet for each child; enlarged (A3) copy of 'Clue words' (p130); individual whiteboards and pens.

Further support
Some children will need the support provided by the 'Clue words' resource sheet for the vocabulary of word problems. They may find it helpful to refer to the list of words when deciding which operation to choose to solve a problem. They may also need an adult to prompt them to remember how to set out each written operation.

Oral and mental starter

Explain that the children are going to play a 'show me' game, using their whiteboards. You are going to read out a question and the children have to listen to the clue words and write the appropriate operation (x, +, ÷, -) on their whiteboards and hold it up for you to see. Ask questions such as: *How many lots of 3 are there in 18? Share 42 between six people. What is 14 less than 82? What is the total of 14, 8 and 9? Find the product of 6 and 4.*

Main assessment activity

Display an A3 copy of the 'Clue words' resource sheet. Discuss what each word means and how it relates to number operations. Point out that not all written questions necessarily require a written calculation. Remind the children of the way they have been working in class - that is, read the question and highlight the clue words. Create a number sum and then decide whether it requires a mental or written strategy to solve it. Estimate first if appropriate and calculate.

Distribute the 'Operation calculate' activity sheet and explain to the children that it is an assessment activity which requires them to make decisions about the operation to choose to solve a problem and also the method that they use. Each child should work independently and use the methods that they are most confident with.

Plenary

Most children should be able to decide on appropriate operations and strategies to solve the word problems. Ask them to explain to a partner how they chose what to do and to discuss the strategies used. An adult should listen to these discussions and record the ways in which individuals are thinking and working.

Name Date

Operation calculate

■ Read the questions carefully and choose the correct operation and method to solve the problems. Use a separate sheet to show your working.

1. Cali has a collection of 182 toy farm animals that she no longer plays with, so she decides to share them between her two cousins. How many toys do they receive each?

2. A farmer doubles his dairy herd from 92 cows. How many cows does he own now?

3. Jay has an autograph book. He went to three separate concerts. At the first he collected 18 signatures, at the second 39 and at the third 27. He already had 30 signatures in his book. How many does he have now?

4. 1056 people visited an exhibition on Friday and 962 on Saturday. What was the total number of visitors?

5. 8926 people went to watch United play in March, but only 6295 attended in April. What was the difference in attendance for the two months?

6. Felt pens are sold in packs of 48. Mrs Jones buys 15 packs for Key Stage 2. How many felt pens did she buy altogether?

7. There are 432 chairs in the hall. They need to be put into groups of 9. How many groups will there be?

8. The animal sanctuary looked after 626 animals last year. They re-housed 194 of them. How many animals are still in need of a new home?

9. There are 72 rows of daffodils in the park. There are 18 in each row. What is the product?

10. The temperature starts at –3°C at 5am but has risen by 15°C by midday. What is the new temperature?

Name Date

Clue words

Addition	**Subtraction**
(answers are bigger than original numbers)	(answers are smaller than original numbers)
add	take away
count on	count back
more than	less than
greater	difference
increase	fewer
total	decrease
sum	remaining
altogether	reduced
risen	fallen

Multiplication	**Division**
(answers are bigger than original numbers)	(answers are smaller than the original numbers)
times	divide
lots of	share
double	halve
increase by	factor
multiply	into groups of
multiple	equal amounts of
product	
altogether	

Name Date

Assessment 6

1. Complete the following:

a) $37 \times 10 =$ **b)** $340 \div 10 =$ **c)** $7490 \div 100 =$

d) $9.3 \times 100 =$ **e)** $16.78 \times 100 =$ **f)** $4.3 \div 10 =$

2. Are the following calculations correct? If not, explain where a mistake has been made and correct it.

a)

	H	T	U
	1	0	9
+	1	8	6
	2	8	5

b)

	H	T	U
	3	6	4
–	1	7	2
	2	1	2

3. Calculate using a written method:

a)

	H	T	U
	1	9	3
+	2	4	6

b)

	H	T	U
	2	5	7
–	1	6	8

Name Date

4. An orchestra has brass instruments worth £7247 and stringed instruments worth £8228. How much is the total value for insurance purposes?

5. I weigh 54 kilograms but my baby brother only weighs 4850 grams. What is the difference between our weights?

ASSESSMENT

End-of-year assessment

There are two forms of end-of-year assessment:

- Mental tests: there are two of these. Each has its own photocopiable sheet on which the children write their answers.
- Check-ups: these are written tests covering all of the key objectives for the year.

The test questions are matched to the key objectives in the table below. Where you are still unsure whether a child has achieved a key objective, use the probing questions in the table for the relevant key objective to help you to make an informed decision about achievement.

Key objective	Mental test 1 question number	Mental test 2 question number	Written test question number	Probing questions
A	18, 19	6	2	*Can you tell me quick way to multiply by 10? What would I multiply 6754 by to make it read 675,400? Does a number get bigger or smaller if we divide it?*
B		7	4, 10	*What information do we use when ordering numbers? Which is bigger: 1264 or 1254? How did you decide? What is the value of the 4 in each number?*
C	13, 14	4, 9, 10		*What is a fraction? How could you describe it? What is $^1/_5$ of 25? What about $^3/_5$? Explain how you calculated this. Which would you prefer, ¼ of a kg of sweets or 0.300kg? How do you know?*
D	4	2, 3, 14		*What does the 4 represent in each of these numbers: 3.4; 4.5; 0.34; 4.04? What if I put a £ sign in front of them? What if they were all lengths given in metres?*
E	1	18	13	*What does rounding mean? Which is greater, 1.4kg or 1.6kg? Why? What number is halfway between 1 and 2 or 200 and 300 or 0 and 1? When do you round up or down? Can you tell me a rule? Can you explain it?*
F	11, 12	1, 8		*What are the digits following a decimal point showing us? What is the first decimal place equal to? What fraction/decimal equivalents do you know?*
G	2, 20	12		*When calculating a difference, what strategy would you use? Can you explain to a friend how to do it?*
H			5, 6, 7, 11	*What are the words associated with word problems that indicate addition or subtraction? How would you check a subtraction sum? What do you do if the digits at the top are bigger than the bottom digits?*
I	5, 6, 7, 8, 9, 10, 15	9, 10, 16, 19	9	*Tell me some factors of 24 or 56. If you know your 2, 3, 5 and 10 times-tables, what else could these help you with? How can times-tables help with division?*
J			1, 3, 8	*What have you got to remember about multiplying by tens? Estimate. Talk me through your method. Do you expect your answer to be greater or smaller than your estimate? Can you spot where I have gone wrong with this calculation?*
K		5, 16, 17, 19, 20	3, 9	*What do you look for when deciding on an operation to use in word problem? What are the clue words?*
L	16, 17	13		*If the area is 24cm², what might the sides be? What does area mean? How can we work out how much space is covered by a 2-D shape?*
M		15		*Tell me some facts about rectangles. What is the same about a square and a rectangle? What is different?*
N		11	12, 14	*Where might you find parallel lines? How can we decide? Show me some parallel lines in this room. What about perpendicular lines?*

Mental maths test 1

Instructions

This mental assessment includes 20 questions which can be given to the children towards the end of the school year.

Setting the test

Provide each child with a copy of the recording sheet for Test 1 (page135). Ask the children to write their names and the date onto the sheet. Explain what will happen as follows:

I am going to ask you some questions. Work out the answer in their head and write down the answer on your sheet. I shall say each question twice and give you a bit of thinking time.

Say the question number then the question twice, leaving a short pause between repetitions. For section A, allow at least 5 seconds thinking time, then move on to the next question. For section B, allow at least 10 seconds thinking time before moving on to the next question. Repeat any questions at the end of the assessment as necessary.

Test 1

Section A

1. Think of one number that could be rounded up to 5000 and one number that could be rounded down to 5000.

2. Subtract 19 from 53.

3. What is three times nine?

4. In the number 16.9, what is the value of the digit nine?

5. What is 6 multiplied by 8?

6. What is eight squared?

7. What is nine lots of 4?

8. What is 27 shared by 3?

9. What is 56 divided by 8?

10. What is the square root of 81?

11. What is the decimal equivalent of $\frac{1}{2}$?

12. What fraction is the same as 0.75?

13. What is three quarters of 20?

14. Half of a number is 35. What is the number?

15. What is double the product of seven and three?

Section B

16. How would you find the area of a rectangle?

17. If a rectangular field measured 15m × 10m, what is its area?

18. What number could I have started with if I multiplied by 100 and the answer is 7800?

19. If I divide 7800 by 10, what number do I have now?

20. I bought a magazine costing two pounds and 65 pence. How much change did I receive from a five pound note?

Name Date

Mental maths test 1 recording sheet

- Listen to the questions, then write your answers in the space provided.

1.		11.	
2.		12.	
3.		13.	
4		14.	
5.		15.	
6.		16.	
7.		17.	
8.		18.	
9.		19.	
10.		20.	

ASSESSMENT

Mental maths test 2

Instructions

This mental assessment includes 20 questions which can be given to the children towards the end of the school year.

Setting the test

Provide each child with a copy of the recording sheet for Test 2 (page137). Ask the children to write their names and the date onto the sheet. Explain what will happen as follows:
I am going to ask you some questions. Work out the answer in their head and write down the answer on your sheet. I shall say each question twice and give you a bit of thinking time.
Say the question number then the question twice, leaving a short pause between repetitions. For section A, allow at least 5 seconds thinking time, then move on to the next question. For section B, allow at least 10 seconds thinking time before moving on to the next question. Repeat any questions at the end of the assessment as necessary.

Test 2

Section A

1. Write this number as a decimal: two hundred and four and six tenths.
2. In the number 345.08, how many hundredths are there?
3. What is the difference between 6.4 and 7?
4. What is half of 1000?
5. How many centimetres in one metre?
6. Multiply 0.85 by 100.
7. If the temperature is 6 degrees Celsius at 8am and rises by 9 degrees by midday, what is the new temperature?
8. What is 23 divided by 2? Write your answer as a decimal fraction.
9. What is one sixth of 42?
10. Find two thirds of 36.

Section B

11. Look at the shapes drawn on your sheet. Tick the shape which has parallel sides.
12. Calculate the difference between 6003 and 2995.
13. What is the area of a rectangle 4cm long and 6cm wide?
14. Look at the numbers on your sheet. Circle the smallest measurement.
15. Think of two statements to complete this sentence: All rectangles have...
16. Kevin had a length of wood 3m 20cm long. He cut it into four equal pieces. How long were the pieces?
17. There are 84 wheels in the car park. Each car has four wheels. How many cars are there altogether?
18. I spent £6.92 at the shop. How much change did I receive from a £10 note?
19. I cut a piece of ribbon into equal pieces. Each piece measures 30cm. I started with a whole length of 2m 10cm. How many pieces do I have?
20. Look at the shapes on your sheet. Put a tick in the scalene triangle.

Name Date

Mental maths test 2 recording sheet

- Listen to the questions, then write your answers in the spaces provided.

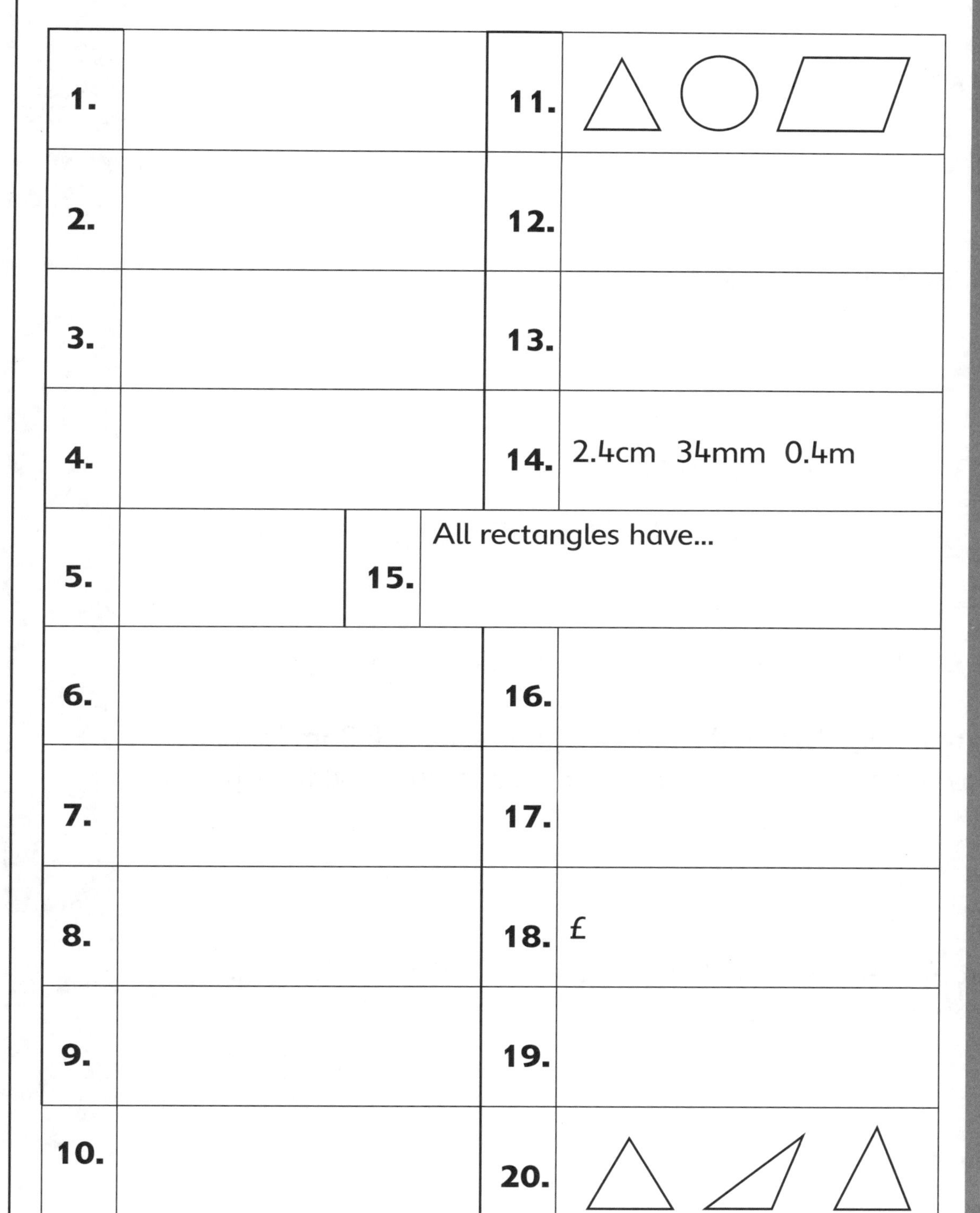

1.		11.	
2.		12.	
3.		13.	
4.		14.	2.4cm 34mm 0.4m
5.		15.	All rectangles have...
6.		16.	
7.		17.	
8.		18.	£
9.		19.	
10.		20.	

Name Date

Check-ups

1. Calculate the following and use a different method to check each answer.

a) $67 \times 4 =$

b) $64 \times 21 =$

2. Fill in the missing numbers:

a) $23 \times$ ____ $= 2300$

b) ____ $\div 10 = 6.9$

c) £1.49 × ____ = £14.90

d) £245 ÷ 100 = ______

3. A man buys 12 lengths of fence panels, each 4.85m long. How long will his fence be when he puts them all together?

4. Put a three-digit number in each box so that the number sentence is correct.

			<	

Name Date

5. Calculate 342 – 169.

6. Annie has collected 834 shells from various holidays; she has 125 more than her sister. How many shells does her sister have in her collection?

7. Annie's sister decides that she doesn't want her shell collection any more and donates all of her shells to Annie. How many does she have altogether?

8. a) 544 ÷ 4 =

b) 291 ÷ 5 =

9. I am thinking of a number. I divide it by 4 and then add 30. My answer is 35. What was my original number?

Name Date

10. Put these numbers in order, smallest first.

0 5 –6 –2 –9 4 –11 –1 1

11. Lucy went collecting donations for her favourite animal charity over six consecutive Saturdays. These are the amounts she collected:

£19.37 £23.14 £35.21 £27.72 £21.96 £30.39

How much did she collect altogether?

12. Draw a shape that has one set of parallel lines and one right angle.

13. Round these numbers to the nearest whole number:

a) 34.19 **b)** 17.03 **c)** 25.51

14. Draw a line perpendicular to this one:

Class record sheet

	Names																	
Key objectives: Year 5																		
Multiply and divide any positive integer up to 10,000 by 10 or 100 and understand the effect.																		
Order a given set of positive and negative integers.																		
Relate fractions to division.																		
Use decimal notation for tenths and hundredths.																		
Round a number with one or two decimal places to the nearest integer.																		
Relate fractions to their decimal representations..																		
Calculate mentally a difference such as 8006 - 2993.																		
Extend written methods to column addition/ subtraction of two integers less than 10,000.																		
Know by heart all multiplication facts up to 10 x 10.																		
Extend written methods to: short multiplication of HTU by U; long multiplication of TU by TU; short division of HTU by U.																		
Use all four operations to solve simple word problems involving numbers and quantities based on 'real life', money and measures (including time).																		
Understand area measured in square centimetres (cm^2). Understand and use the formula in words 'length x breadth' for the area of a rectangle.																		
Recognise properties of rectangles.																		
Recognise perpendicular and parallel lines.																		

Answer sheet

Autumn term

P87 Hold the place value! 1 100. **2** 84. **3** 21. **4** 100. **5** 7.2. **6** 3.4. **7** 260. **8** 0.5. **9** 100. **10** 36. **11** 17.6. **12** 3.45. **13** 10. **14** 3740. **15** and **16** any correct combination.

P89 Decimal ducks and drakes As they work, check that the children are matching the correct fractions to the decimals.

P91 Assessment test: autumn half-term 1
1 Axis label x = days of the week; axis label y = number of children. Title = A graph to show the number of children who brought a packed lunch in one week. Bars should indicate 15 on Thursday and 12 on Friday.
a) Mode = Monday. **b)** 20 - 12 = 8.
2a) 13th and 14th days were the hottest; **b)** 9th day was the coolest; **c)** On the second day the temperature reached 14°C.

P95 When is a rectangle not a rectangle? Shapes 1 and 3 are rectangles since they match all the properties; number 1 is a square, a special rectangle, having two pairs of sides, all of equal length.

P97 Count on me! 1 2002. **2** 4003. **3** 2026. **4** 4116. **5** 4175. **6** 4042. **7** 721. **8** 2035. **9** 1007. **10** 3128.

P99 Assessment test: autumn half-term 2
1 Two sets of parallel lines; four right angles; each pair of parallel lines are of equal length; diagonals bisect in the middle; there are two lines of symmetry.
2a) 1111; **b)** 1265; **c)** 1487.
3a) The mistake they are making is that they are taking the smaller digit from the larger digit irrespective of whether they take the top digit from the bottom or vice versa.
b) The mistake here is that they are adding instead of subtracting.
4a) 4684 (addition); **b)** 1034 (subtraction); **c)** £736.45 (subtraction or find the difference).

Spring term

P103 The great divide 1 147. **2** 208. **3** 143. **4** 32. **5** 151. **6** 117. **7** 170 r 1. **8** 302 r 2. **9** 116. **10** 22 r 5.

P105 Divide it up and share it out!

6	5	6	6	9
8	10	8	7	6
7	8	8	1	3
6	3	5	4	8
10	7	6	4	6

P107 Assessment test: spring half-term 1
1 132; 214; 150 r2 or $150\frac{1}{2}$ or 150.5.
2a) This person has forgotten to move the 200 along to be with the 3 tens, making 23 tens to be divided. **b)** This person has correctly seen 10 ÷ 5 = 2 but has then gone on to divide the 0 again and so put another zero in the answer. Otherwise it would be correct. Incomplete understanding of place value. **c)** This person has muddled their times-tables and said that 2 × 8 = 8.
3a) 22 (division); **b)** £144 (multiplication), then £126 (subtraction); **c)** 236 cars (division), then 1008 wheels (multiplication and addition).
4a) 8; **b)** 27; **c)** 9; **d)** 20; **e)** 7; **f)** 45.
5

horizontal line
two parallel perpendicular lines

6 50°, 125°, 23°.

P111 This is my area! Answers will vary, but check calculations.

P113 It all adds up! 1 565. **2** £146.69. **3** 625. **4** £22.16. **5** 1345. **6** £113.19. **7** 828. **8** £51.61. **9** 19.55m. **10** £19.47.

P115 Assessment test: spring half-term 2
1 40cm².
2 8×4cm or 16×2cm or 32×1cm.
3 No. A square must have all four sides the same length. Therefore a square with sides measuring 7×7 would have an area of 49cm².
4 Length × breadth.
5a) 871; **b)** 1553; **c)** 538; **d)** 467.
6a) Correct answer is 609. Person forgot to add on the 'carried' 10 from 8 + 2 = 10.
b) Correct answer is 684. The mistake here is that the smaller digit is being taken away from the larger digit irrespective of whether they take the top digit from the bottom or vice versa.
7 740.
8 Jennie earned £180, Ann earned £102.

Answer sheet

Summer term

P119 The long multiplication road 1 504. **2** 486. **3** 945. **4** 1224. **5** 805. **6** 1728. **7** 1825. **8** 1764. **9** 375. **10** 1148.

P121 Equal shares for all Dominoes should match touching ends fraction to decimal.

Top: 0.4 | $\frac{1}{10}$ — 0.1 | $\frac{8}{10}$ — $\frac{80}{100}$ | 0.2 — $\frac{1}{5}$ | 0.75

Right side: $\frac{3}{4}$ | 0.3 — $\frac{30}{100}$ | 0.5

Bottom: $\frac{1}{2}$ | 0.4 — $\frac{4}{10}$ | 0.7 — $\frac{7}{10}$ | 0.6 — $\frac{60}{100}$ | $\frac{10}{10}$

Left side: 1.0 | $\frac{1}{4}$ — 0.25 | $\frac{4}{10}$

P123 Assessment test: summer half-term 1

1a) 765; **b)** 608.

```
HTU
 53
x 15
 15  ✓
 25  × Not showing place value
  3  × Place value (x10)
  5  × Place value (10 x 50)
 48

HTU
 53
x 15
 15
 30
250
500
795

HTU
 64
x 23
192  ✓
128  × Place value holder missing
320

HTU
  64
x 23
 192
1280
1472
```

3 518.
4a) 384; **b)** £30.72.
5a) 9; **b)** 41; **c)** 9; **d)** 6; **e)** 6; **f)** 4.5.
6 8.
7a) 3:2; **b)** 27 toffees.

P127 You can't take the top from the bottom! **1** 864; **2** 3561; **3** 1108; **4** 1806; **5** 2888; **6** £232.74; **7** £46.79; **8** £66.98; **9** £63.20; **10** 209.

P129 Operation calculate **1** 91. **2** 184. **3** 114. **4** 2018. **5** 2631. **6** 720. **7** 48. **8** 432. **9** 1296. **10** 12°C.

P131 Assessment test: summer half-term 2
1a) 370; **b)** 34; **c)** 74.9; **d)** 930; **e)** 1678; **f)** 0.43.
2a) This person has forgotten to add on the 'carried 10 from 9 + 6 = 15. **b)** This person has taken away the smaller digit, irrespective of whether it is the top or the bottom digit.
3a) 439; **b)** 89.
4 £15,475.
5 49.15kg or 49,150 grams.

End-of-year assessment

P134 Mental maths test 1
1 4500 to 5449. **2** 34. **3** 27.
4 Nine tenths. **5** 48. **6** 64.
7 36. **8** 9. **9** 7. **10** 9. **11** 0.5.
12 Three quarters. **13** 15. **14** 70.
15 42. **16** Length × breadth.
17 150m². **18** 78. **19** 780. **20** £2.35.

P136 Mental maths test 2
1 204.6. **2** 8. **3** 0.6.
4 500. **5** 100. **6** 85.
7 17°C. **8** 11.5. **9** 7. **10** 24.
11 Parallelogram (third shape).
12 3008. **13** 24cm². **14** 2.4cm.
15 Four right angles, two pairs of sides which are equal in length but different from the length of the other pair, diagonals that intersect in the centre.
16 80cm. **17** 21. **18** £3.08. **19** 7.
20 The middle triangle (scalene) should be ticked.

P138 Check-ups
1a) 268; **b)** 1344 (check methods used).
2a) 23 × 100 = 2300; **b)** 69 ÷ 10 = 6.9; **c)** £1.49 × 10 = £14.90; **d)** £245 ÷ 100 = £2.45.
3 58.2m.
4 Any plausible numbers to make an accurate sentence.
5 173 (check method used).
6 709.
7 709 + 834 = 1543.
8a) 136; **b)** 58 r 1 or $58\frac{1}{5}$ or 58.2.
9 20.
10 -11, -9, -6, -2, -1, 0, 1, 4, 5.
11 £157.79.
12 Check that the shape fits the criteria.
13a) 34; **b)** 17; **c)** 6.
14 Ensure that the drawn line is at right angles to the given line.

SCHOLASTIC

In this series:

ISBN 0-439-96512-8
ISBN 978-0439-96512-5

ISBN 0-439-96513-6
ISBN 978-0439-96513-2

ISBN 0-439-96514-4
ISBN 978-0439-96514-9

ISBN 0-439-965152
ISBN 978-0439-96515-6

ISBN 0-439-965160
ISBN 978-0439-96516-3

ISBN 0-439-965179
ISBN 978-0439-96517-0

ISBN 0-439-965187
ISBN 978-0439-96518-7